GCSE Statistics

The Workbook

This book contains lots of tricky questions designed
to make you sweat — because that's
the only way you'll get better.

It's also got some daft bits in to try and make the whole
experience at least vaguely entertaining for you.

Contents

Section One — Data Collection

Section Two — Tabulation and Representation

Section Three — Data Analysis

Section Four — Probability

Published by Coordination Group Publications Ltd.

Contributors: Andrew Ballard, Sally Gill, Tim Major, Val Malcolm, Sam Norman, Ali Palin, Andy Park, Katherine Reed, Alan Rix, Mark Turner, Julie Wakeling, Sharon Watson, Janet West

ISBN: 978 1 84146 422 0
Groovy website: www.cgpbooks.co.uk

With thanks to Vicky Daniel and Glenn Rogers for the proofreading.

Printed by Elanders Hindson Ltd, Newcastle upon Tyne.

Questions on Data Sources

Q1 Say whether each of these data collection methods gives primary or secondary data.

a) Using unprocessed data from the 1901 census.

b) Doing an experiment to see how long students take to complete a puzzle.

c) Using temperature charts from a national newspaper.

Q2 a) Write down one way of collecting secondary data.

b) Write down one disadvantage of using secondary data.

Q3 In 1999 the Wonderme cosmetics company claimed that its anti-wrinkle cream was more effective than any other on the market. In 2003 a beauty salon used the Wonderme statistics when deciding which anti-wrinkle cream to promote.

a) Is the data used by the beauty salon primary or secondary data?

b) Give two disadvantages of using these statistics.

Q4 Complete the table saying whether the data is primary or secondary.

Data	Primary or Secondary
Data from the 2001 census on the number of rooms in a house.	
Results from an experiment measuring sizes of spider webs.	
A pie chart in a magazine showing preferred beauty products.	
A grouped frequency table compiled by a supermarket showing the number of times customers visit the supermarket each month	

Remember — primary data is raw; secondary data has been processed.

Q5 A market research company collects data on the amount spent on clothes per week by all the people living on Rosamund Street. The table below shows the ages of the people interviewed.

Age	Under 18	18-30	31-45	46-60	Over 60
Frequency	2	13	12	20	53

Cuthbert finds the company's data when he is doing research on how school children spend their pocket money.

a) Is this primary or secondary data?

b) Give one reason why Cuthbert should not use this data.

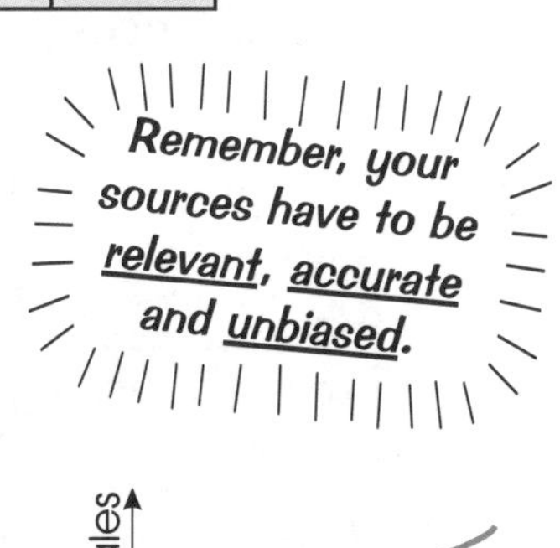

Q6 Phloggit Advertising have compiled a graph to show how they have improved the sales figures of their client, Swindluz Sweets. Kate is thinking about using this graph as a data source for her business studies project on marketing methods.

a) Give one criticism of this piece of data.

b) Say whether the graph is primary or secondary data.

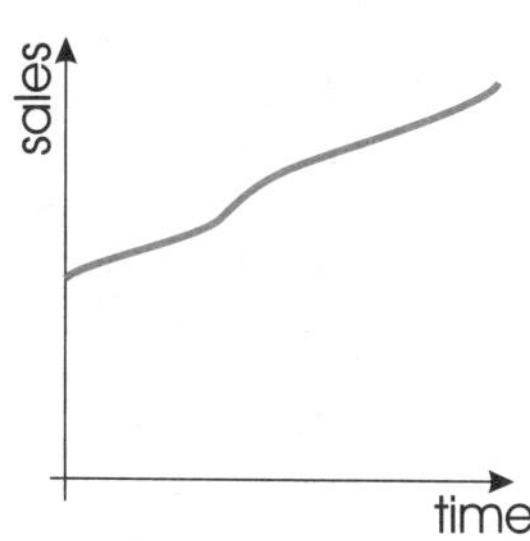

Questions on Types of Data

Data can be qualitative or quantitative, discrete or continuous — know the differences.

Q1 **a)** Write down a definition of quantitative data.

b) What is the name given to data which can't be measured numerically?

Q2 Zac collects some data about his school. The data items are listed below. Say whether each data item is qualitative or quantitative.

a) The colours of pants worn by the teachers.

b) The number of students late to school from each form on the first day of term.

c) The distance travelled to school by each student.

d) The star sign of each student.

Q3 **a)** What name is given to quantitative data that can be measured exactly?

b) Give one example of this type of data.

c) Write down a definition of continuous data.

d) Give one example of continuous data.

Q4 A music shop sells CDs, DVDs, tapes and some vinyl records.

a) State one example of qualitative data that could be collected by the shop.

b) State one example of quantitative data that could be collected by the shop.

Q5 Amy collects some data at her school sports day. The data items are listed below. Say whether each data item is discrete or continuous.

a) The number of competitors in each event.

b) The finishing times of each competitor in the 100-metre sprint.

c) The total number of points scored by each form at the end of the day.

d) The distances jumped by each competitor in the long jump.

Q6 Complete the table saying which type of data has been used.

Data	Discrete or Continuous
Tail-bone lengths of dinosaurs collected in archaeological sites in America	
Number of people passing through Heathrow airport each day.	
Number of red blood cells in a collection of 10 ml blood samples.	
Times taken to be served in a fast-food restaurant.	

Don't forget: if you can measure a quantity exactly then it's discrete — otherwise it's continuous.

Questions on Classifying Data

Q1 Ben is collecting data about the clothes people are buying.
He splits the clothes into five classes — nice clothes, OK clothes, rubbish clothes, only-fit-for-the-bin clothes and shoes.

a) Give one criticism of Ben's choice of classes.

b) List five well-defined classes that Ben could split the clothes into.

Edexcel only

Q2 **a)** Write down a definition of a categorical scale of measurement.

b) A general collects data on the numbers of each rank of soldier in the army.
The data is recorded in the table below.

Rank	Frequency
1	18,500
2	13,100
3	9,200
4	4,800

Key
1 – Private
2 – Lance Corporal
3 – Corporal
4 – Sergeant

i) What type of scale of measurement is the general using?
ii) Are lance corporals twice as good as privates?

Edexcel only

Q3 Data is collected at a fast-food restaurant. Decide which type of scale (categorical, rank, interval or ratio) would be best for each set of data:

Higher

a) The temperatures in °C of the cups of coffee sold.

b) The types of burger bought (hamburger, cheese burger, quarter pounder, etc.)

c) Marks out of 5 given by customers filling in customer satisfaction forms.

d) The amount in pounds spent by each customer.

Edexcel only

Q4 The tables below show data collected at a stationery shop.
Say what type of scale of measurement is used for each table.

a) Hardness of pencils sold

Hardness	1	2	3	4	5
Number of pencils sold	10	22	45	36	8

Key
1 – Very soft
2 – Moderately soft
3 – Average
4 – Moderately hard
5 – Very hard

b) Types of A4 pads of paper sold

Type of A4 pad	1	2	3	4
Number of pads sold	51	74	20	8

Key
1 – lined without margin
2 – lined with margin
3 – plain white
4 – coloured

Don't forget — the four types of scale are categorical, rank, interval and ratio.

Higher

c) Weights of novelty erasers

Weight of eraser (grams)	0-10	10-20	20-40	More than 40
Frequency	3	18	35	10

Higher

Q5 **a)** Write down a definition of an interval scale of measurement.

b) Give one example of an interval scale of measurement.

Questions on More Types of Data

Q1 The table shows the number of coins in the pockets of a random sample of 100 people.

Number of coins	0-5	6-10	11-15	16-30
Frequency	44	26	19	11

a) What are the lower class limits?

b) What are the class intervals in the table?

Q2 Fred asked each of his 30 classmates how long (in minutes) it took them to eat their dinner. Here are the results he recorded:

42	13	3	31	15	20	19	1	59	14
8	25	16	27	4	55	32	31	31	10
32	17	16	19	29	42	43	30	29	18

a) Use the data to complete a copy of this grouped frequency table.

b) State one disadvantage of grouping data.

Length of time (mins)	1-10	11-20	21-30	31-40	41-60
Frequency					

Q3 The table below shows the percentage marks of a group of students in an English exam, and the number of words each student wrote.

Student	A	B	C	D	E	F	G	H	I	J
Percentage Mark	10	91	78	65	56	59	35	68	42	49
Number of words	35	588	412	376	380	401	221	392	290	307

a) How many students' marks are recorded?

b) Say whether this statement is true or false — "Only 1 student got less than 40%"

c) How many words did the student who got 91% write?

Q4 Census data on household incomes and the number of rooms per home is given in the table.

Household income per month (£)	Number of rooms in home				Total
	Fewer than 4	4-6	7-8	More than 8	
Less than 500	5	10	1	0	16
500-999	7	7	2	0	16
1000-1499	2	15	1	1	19
1500-1999	5	2	7	4	18
2000 or more	3	0	5	3	11
Total	22	34	16	8	80

a) How many of the homes have more than 8 rooms?

b) How many of the households have an income of less than £500 per month?

c) How many of the households with an income of £2000 or more per month have fewer than four rooms?

Q5 Say whether the data described below is discrete bivariate data or continuous bivariate data.

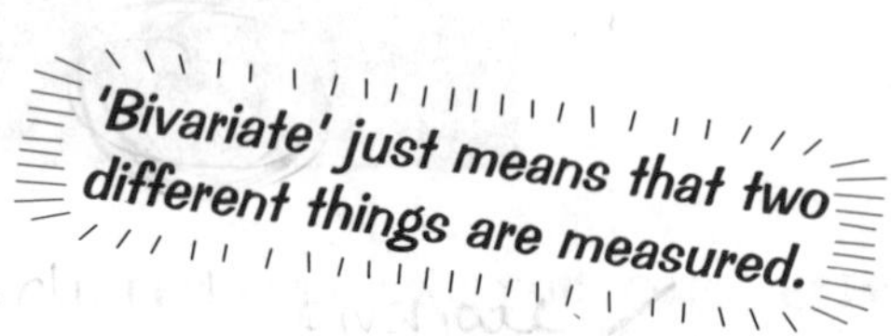

a) Shoe size and marks out of 20 scored in a science test.

b) Heights and tail lengths of lesser spotted ferrets.

Questions on Census Data

Make sure you know what your population is — you can't do anything without that.

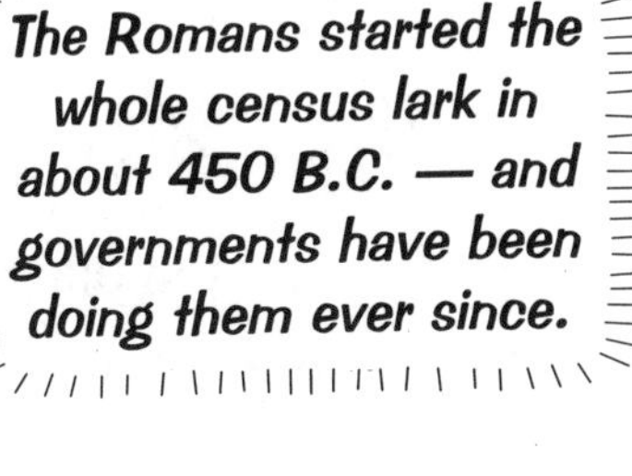

Q1 Write down a definition of the term 'population'.

Q2 Say what the population is for each of these surveys:

a) The health effects of smoking on 20- to 30-year-old women.

b) The number of trees in public parks in London.

c) The average number of hours British squirrels spend juggling nuts.

d) The pay of football players in the Premier League.

Q3 Write down a definition of the term 'census'.

Q4 Stripy swamp alligator males and females are indistinguishable until they reach 2 years of age.

Give one reason why it would be difficult to carry out a census on the tail lengths of male stripy swamp alligators aged between 0 and 5 years.

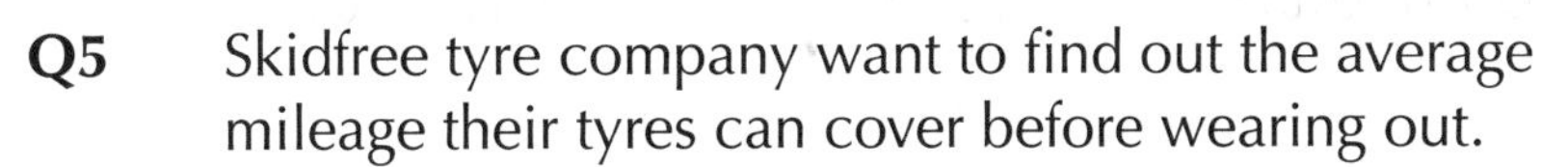

Q5 Skidfree tyre company want to find out the average mileage their tyres can cover before wearing out.

a) Would the Skidfree tyre company use a census to find out this information?

b) Give a reason for your answer to part a).

Q6 Lancashire County Council want to carry out a census of their residents to find out information such as employment, income, and size of household.

a) What is the population for this census?

b) State one problem that they might encounter while doing this.

Q7 Moreton United speed-basketweaving club have a very large number of supporters. They want to find out whether sponsorship influences their supporters' shopping habits.

a) What population should Moreton United use for their project?

b) Give one reason why it would be difficult for the club to carry out a census.

Q8 Professor Xavier Entric is doing a research project on the lifespan of moorland dung beetles in the UK.

a) What population would Professor Entric use for his research?

b) Give one reason why Professor Entric would not use a census.

Questions on Sampling

You've got to be able to spot problems and criticise sampling techniques — basically, if you think it's a load of rubbish, you need to be able to say why.

Q1 Sometimes it is not possible or practical to carry out a census — you need to use a sample instead.

a) What is "sampling"?

b) Give two advantages of using sampling instead of a census.

Q2 James wants to know the average weekly wage earned by teenagers in his town. He calculates the mean from the weekly wages of three of his classmates at school.

Give two reasons why this sample may not give him a true estimate of the average wage for the town.

Q3 The table below shows a breakdown of the ages of 100 people interviewed by a pollster on Trumpwick high street on a Monday morning.

Age	Under 18	18-35	36-50	51-60	More than 60
Frequency	0	8	26	34	32

Give one reason why this would not be a good sample to use for a survey about the nightclubs in Trumpwick.

Q4 A car manufacturer sends out a questionnaire to all 1000 purchasers of a car. 400 people reply, of which 300 say that they are completely satisfied with the car and 100 say that there has been some kind of fault with the car.

a) The car manufacturer says:

"75% of our customers are completely satisfied with this car"

Give one criticism of this statement.

b) What is the smallest possible percentage of customers in the sample who are completely satisfied with the car?

Q5 a) Give one advantage of using census data instead of sample data.

b) 100 names are chosen at random from a telephone book. Give one reason why this might not be an appropriate sample to use to find out about the incomes of people living in the area covered by the telephone book.

Questions on Sampling

Q6 Beth comes from a family of 10 children. For an IT project at school she is asked to collect data on the types of IT the students in her school have access to at home. Beth decides to collect data by surveying her brothers and sisters.

Give one reason why this is not a good sample to use.

Remember — a sample is pretty useless if it isn't representative of the population.

Q7 A Year 11 class are collecting data about the distance that members of teaching staff travel to get to their school in the morning. They each survey a sample of 30 teachers chosen at random from a list of all the teachers in their school.

Here are John and Kelly's results:

John's Results

Distance travelled	No. of people
Less than 1 mile	卌 ||||
Between 1 and 3 miles	卌 |
Between 4 and 6 miles	卌 |
Between 6 and 9 miles	|||
10 miles or more	卌 |

Kelly's Results

Distance travelled	No. of people
Less than 1 mile	卌 卌 |
Between 1 and 3 miles	卌 |||
Between 4 and 6 miles	卌
Between 6 and 9 miles	||
10 miles or more	||||

John and Kelly selected their samples from the same sample frame.
Explain why their tables are not identical.

The key to really good sampling is a well-defined population and sample frame — it's important these are right so that your results are representative of the population.

Q8 Write down a definition of the term "sample frame".

Q9 Whitby football club are trying to find out about how much their supporters are prepared to spend on merchandise.

a) What population should Whitby football club sample from?

The football club prepare a questionnaire and send it to 1000 people chosen at random from the electoral register of Whitby.

b) What population have Whitby football club used as a sample frame?

c) Give one criticism of the way that Whitby football club have chosen their sample.

Questions on Sampling

Q10 An environmental group is investigating the water quality in all the lakes and ponds in Nottingham.

a) What population should the environmental group use?

b) What should they use as a sample frame?

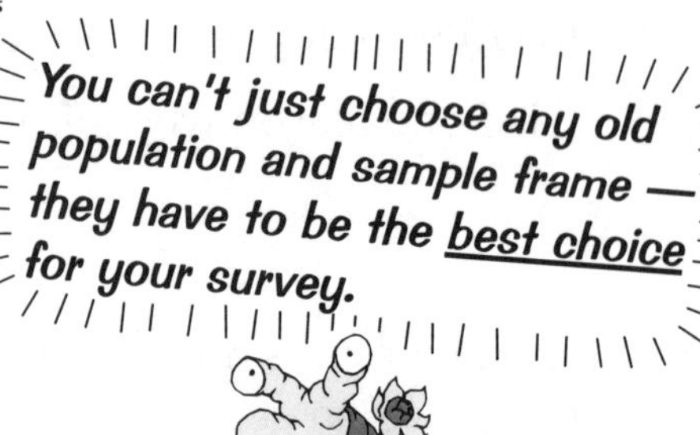

Q11 Describe how you would choose a simple random sample of 500 people from a list of 4000 names.

Q12 A bakery makes 50 Battenburg cakes every day.

The quality controller tests the cakes every Friday for weight and tastiness.
She can only use a sample of 5 cakes because the cakes get eaten in the tastiness test.

a) Each week the quality controller chooses the first 5 cakes off the production line for her sample. What is wrong with this method?

b) On one Friday, all the cakes are weighed, giving the following results:

201 g	203 g	206 g	194 g	203 g
206 g	197 g	196 g	206 g	189 g
205 g	201 g	211 g	222 g	204 g
212 g	195 g	206 g	202 g	198 g
198 g	197 g	204 g	203 g	201 g
194 g	208 g	194 g	203 g	184 g
198 g	204 g	196 g	199 g	204 g
194 g	203 g	198 g	199 g	194 g
206 g	201 g	205 g	201 g	194 g
205 g	202 g	199 g	195 g	198 g

Describe how you would choose a simple random sample of 5 cake weights.
You must state how you would select the cake weights.

Q13 An internet book company want to find out about the reading habits of their customers. They send a questionnaire out to 1000 people chosen at random from the Rochdale telephone book. Give a criticism of the sample they have chosen.

Questions on Systematic & Stratified Sampling

Higher

Q1 Explain how you would use systematic sampling to get a sample of 500 from a telephone directory containing 20 000 names.

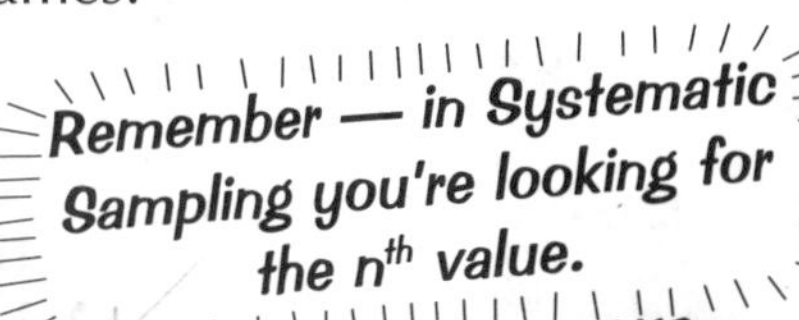

Higher

Q2 Give one advantage and one disadvantage of using systematic sampling over stratified sampling.

Q3 The Instyle chain of hair salons employs 1000 people across the UK. Of these, 99 are receptionists, 53 are salon managers, 251 are colour technicians and the rest are stylists. They decide to use a stratified sample of 100 to find out about employee satisfaction.

a) How many of each type of employee should be in the sample?

b) Give one reason why it is better for the Instyle chain to use a stratified random sample than a simple random sample.

Q4 Fred is doing a statistical project on the distances travelled by students to his school. He gives a questionnaire to a sample of 30 of his friends in Year 10.

a) Give one criticism of Fred's sample.

b) The table below gives a breakdown of the numbers of students in each year group at Fred's school.

Year Group	7	8	9	10	11
Number of Students	398	405	401	197	199

If Fred takes a stratified random sample with 40 students, how many Year 7 students would be in the sample?

Don't forget that the proportion of any group in a sample has to be the same as the proportion in the population.

c) In another stratified random sample from the same school, there are ten Year 11 students. How many students are in the sample altogether?

Higher

Q5 The table below shows the breakdown of staff in a large chain of restaurants.

	Waiting Staff	Bar Staff	Chefs	Managers
Male	297	199	398	49
Female	704	202	102	49

a) For an efficiency study, the restaurant management use a stratified random sample of 50 employees. They use two sets of categories.

i) How many male waiting staff should be in the sample?

ii) How many female bar staff should be in the sample?

b) In another stratified random sample with the same two sets of categories, there are 20 male chefs. How large is the sample?

Questions on Data Logging

Data logging is simply the automatic collection of raw data at given intervals by a machine. Basically, you tell the data logger what you want to record, and how often, and away it goes — this is really handy when you need to take loads of measurements.

Q1 The council use a data logger to record the speed of traffic passing through a village. The first 100 values recorded by the data logger are displayed in the table below.

16	37	57	1	54	20	67	87	97	48
98	47	99	30	69	86	77	31	62	37
74	40	55	81	46	43	74	93	49	65
64	68	27	85	10	47	69	37	24	56
64	27	69	96	98	13	50	27	47	93
99	12	23	29	75	31	20	87	17	68
26	54	39	64	12	89	90	55	80	41
15	25	85	25	14	36	90	54	59	88
49	84	53	7	84	36	30	31	20	41
72	9	28	52	36	6	84	96	12	23

Data loggers can be programmed to use systematic sampling on the data they record.

a) The road safety officer wants to see more than 20 but fewer than 30 items of data, so programs the data logger to select every n^th^ number from the table, reading line by line from left to right. What value of n does the data logger use?

b) List the values that the data logger produces, using the rule from a).

Q2 Would you use a data logger in the following situations? Say why.

a) Taking five measurements of the weight of a melting ice block.

b) Measuring the speed of a car every 10 seconds, for an hour.

c) Counting the number of customers entering a shop, over a weekend.

d) Measuring the time taken for 20 students to peel a banana.

Q3 A camera is set up to monitor both payment tills in a busy shop. The camera takes a photograph every ten minutes, and the total number of customers seen waiting at the tills is counted in each picture. The results are shown below.

2, 1, 3, 7, 5, 3, 4, 8, 2, 8, 7, 6, 10, 7, 11, 8, 13, 12, 9, 10, 4, 6, 2, 4.

a) Give one advantage of collecting data only once every ten minutes.

b) Give one disadvantage of this method of data collection.

c) Over what period of time does the data appear to have been collected?

d) The shopkeeper calculates that the mean number of people at the tills during this time is 6 (to the nearest whole number). Why might this not be an accurate figure?

e) She also says that 13 people at the tills at once is the busiest the shop got in that period. Why might she be wrong?

Questions on Cluster & Quota Sampling

This page and the next are for Higher only, so all you Foundation people can ignore this lot and skip straight to page 13.

Higher **Q1** Describe a method using cluster sampling to get a sample of 1000 people for a market research survey using all the telephone books in the UK.

Give a brief justification for the method you've chosen.

Higher **Q2** A large furniture shop carries out a survey to find out about the requirements of its customers. They consider three ways of getting a sample of 2000 people.

For each method, say whether cluster, quota or convenience sampling is being used:

a) The company ask a researcher to interview 2000 people visiting the shop. Of these, 500 must be aged less than 30, 500 must be 30 to 40, 500 must be 40 to 60 and 500 must be over 60.

b) The first 2000 people to enter the shop on the first Saturday in March are interviewed.

c) The company randomly selects 10 postal districts from all the postal districts within a 50-mile radius of the shop. 20 households are chosen at random from each postal district.

Q3 A theme park carries out a survey on which rides are the most popular.

a) Describe how they could use convenience sampling to obtain a sample of 500 people.

b) Discuss one problem the company might face in using this method of sampling.

Cluster, Quota and Convenience sampling methods are used because they're cheap as chips and easy as pie... hmmm, it must be nearly lunchtime...

Q4 Professor Zhargle is investigating the chemical composition of meteorites. He chooses a random sample of 10 museums with meteorite collections and then chooses 10 random meteorites from each collection.

What type of sampling is Professor Zhargle using?

Q5 In the 2001 census, 390,000 people in England and Wales gave their religion as "Jedi Knight". This is 0.7% of the total population.

You are carrying out a survey which requires your sample to give a fair representation of all the stated religious beliefs in England and Wales.

How many Jedi Knights would you have to include in a sample of size 1000?

Obiwan has taught you well... but you are not a statistician yet.

Questions on Strengths & Weaknesses of Sampling

Just knowing all the different sampling methods isn't enough — you've got to be able to say what's good and bad about each method... if you're doing Higher that is.

Q1 The makers of Ken and Merrie's Ice cream suspect that one of their tub-filling machines is faulty. They think that it is overfilling every fifth tub. Give one reason why it would not be useful for them to use systematic random sampling to check this.

Q2 A market research company designs a questionnaire that must be answered by face-to-face interview. They choose a random sample of 2000 people using a list of households covered in the 2001 census as a sample frame.

a) What type of sampling are they using?

b) Give one advantage and one disadvantage of the company using this type of sampling.

Q3 The Department of Tourism wishes to carry out a survey into different types of holiday accommodation in England and Wales. They select 20 counties at random and survey 50 postal districts chosen at random from each county.

a) What type of sampling has the Department of Tourism used?

b) State one problem the Department of Tourism might face with their sample.

Q4 Dennis is carrying out a survey into the diet of the people who live in his town. He stands outside his local Bigburger fast-food restaurant and interviews the first 500 people to pass him.

a) What type of sampling has Dennis used?

b) State one problem Dennis might face with the data he gets from this sample.

Q5 The headmaster of a secondary school wants to find out the views of the parents on school uniform. He thinks of two methods of selecting a sample of 50 parents:

1 – Interview the first 50 parents to drop their children off at school in the morning.

2 – Select the sample from a list of all parents of children at the school, making sure that the proportions from each year group are representative of the proportions in the school.

a) Which of the two methods will give a biased sample?

b) Give one reason for your answer to part a).

c) What is the name given to the type of sampling used for the unbiased method?

Q6 State one problem that can arise when attempting to use stratified random sampling.

Q7 **a)** Describe a situation where quota sampling rather than stratified sampling has to be used.

b) State one disadvantage of quota sampling.

Questions on Biased Samples

Most of these samples have been taken from the wrong population. You need to be able to work out which population has actually been sampled, and compare it to the target population.

Q1 Millom University Chemistry Department wants to find out the influence of its marketing on sixth-form chemistry students in the UK. They compile a survey and send it to all the students at the nearest sixth-form college.

a) Give two reasons why this sample is biased.

b) What population should the Millom University Chemistry Department be sampling from?

Q2 The Cheapeez discount food chain wants to find out what products to stock to attract more of the residents of Devon. Their interviewers survey the first 200 people to go into five Cheapeez supermarkets in Devon on the first Saturday in March.

a) Give one reason why this sample will produce biased data.

b) What population should have been sampled from?

Q3 The table below shows a breakdown of the age groups of the residents of Yeovil.

Age	Under 18	18-30	31-40	41-60	Over 60
Percentage of population	23%	17%	12%	32%	16%

The local council wants to find out whether their residents prefer to shop at out-of-town shopping centres or on Yeovil High Street. They put together a questionnaire and interview a sample of 1000 people shopping on Yeovil High Street on Saturday morning. The sample contains 205 people aged 30 or under, 421 people aged 31 to 40, 199 people aged 41 to 60 and 175 over-60s.

a) Write down two reasons why this sample is biased.

b) What population should the council have sampled from?

Higher → **Q4** Four types of sampling are listed below.

Simple random sampling	Stratified sampling
Cluster sampling	Systematic sampling

a) Which type of sampling is most likely to produce a biased sample?

b) Give a reason for your answer to part a).

Q5 Fred is trying to find out why people use public transport.
He surveys a sample of 100 people passing through the town bus station between 5.30 p.m. and 6.30 p.m. on a Monday evening.

a) Give one reason why Fred's sample is biased.

b) Say how Fred could improve his sample to avoid bias.

Questions on Planning an Investigation

You must state a <u>hypothesis</u> when planning an investigation — this will <u>explain</u> clearly what you think is <u>going to happen</u>.

Q1 Last year the Freezee ice-cream company ran a leafleting campaign to promote their products. They want to investigate whether the campaign was successful. State a hypothesis that the Freezee ice-cream company should test to investigate the success of their campaign.

Q2 Rod, Jane and Eddie are playing a card game. Rod and Jane think that Eddie is cheating by stacking the deck because he has won 9 games out of 10. State a hypothesis that Rod and Jane could test to investigate their theory that Eddie is cheating.

Q3 The Fixit drug company have discovered a new drug which they call "Poxfix". They think that Poxfix could be a cure for chickenpox. What hypothesis should the Fixit drug company test to see if Poxfix works?

Q4 A sports scientist thinks that the more TV students watch, the more likely they are to be overweight and do badly in exams. State two hypotheses that the scientist should test to see if he is right.

Q5 Pete is investigating the effects of regular exercise on resting pulse rate for his PE coursework. His hypothesis is:

People who exercise for at least 20 minutes three times per week or more have a lower resting pulse rate than those who do not.

a) What data should Pete collect to test this hypothesis?

b) When testing the hypothesis, Pete finds his results neither support nor conflict with his hypothesis. Give one reason why this may have happened.

c) What should Pete do to avoid this problem?

Q6 Mrs. Counter the statistics teacher thinks that when her students attend extra revision classes after school, their performance at Statistics GCSE improves.

a) What hypothesis should Mrs. Counter test to investigate the effectiveness of the revision classes.

A student in Mrs. Counter's class investigates the results of last year's GCSE. He finds that in general, students who didn't attend the extra classes got higher grades than those who did.

b) Give one reason why this could have happened.

c) How could the effectiveness of the revision class be tested?

Questions on Planning an Investigation

Questionnaires, experiments, primary and secondary data are all terms you'll need for this page — so make sure you know them.

Q7 The management of a boy band want to find out if their assumptions about the band's fans are true. They decide to test this hypothesis:

The majority of fans are girls aged between 7 and 13.

How could the management of the band collect data to test their hypothesis?

Q8 The makers of Raz washing powder claim that their washing powder cleans whiter than any other brand.

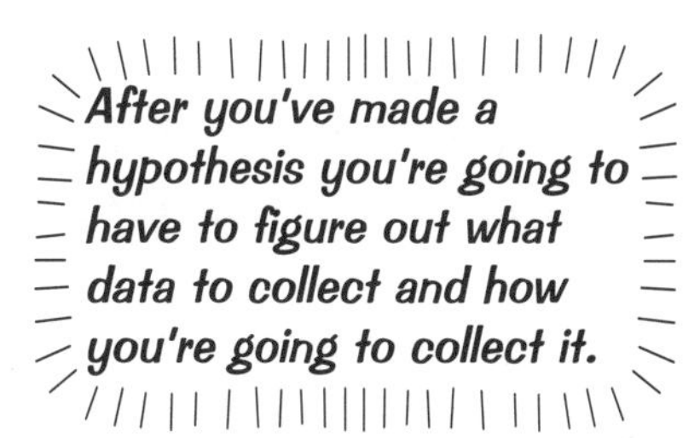

a) Write down a hypothesis that the Raz manufacturers could test to see if their claim is true or not.

b) How could the makers of Raz test this hypothesis?

Q9 South Lakeland District Council is trying to encourage more people to recycle paper, glass and cans. They want to see if recycling levels have been improved by a collection service that they have set up.

a) What hypothesis should the council use to test whether recycling levels have improved?

b) Describe one way in which the council could test the hypothesis.

Q10 A health authority is concerned about the sale of sweets and crisps in schools. They think that this could lead to higher numbers of overweight students.

a) State a hypothesis that the health authority could test to see if they are correct.

b) To test their hypothesis the health authority collect data from two schools:

A sports academy which has vending machines and a tuck shop.

A comprehensive which does not sell sweets and crisps to students.

Give one criticism of this data.

c) How could the health authority test their hypothesis in a more reliable way?

Q11 The police want to investigate whether or not road traffic accidents are more likely to occur during the morning rush hour (between 8 a.m and 9 a.m.) than any other time of day.

a) Write down a hypothesis that the police could test for their investigation.

b) Describe how a questionnaire could be used to collect data to test the hypothesis.

c) State another source of raw data that could be used to test the hypothesis.

Questions on Questionnaires

Q1 The government wants to find out about drug use by inmates of prisons. A questionnaire is designed which will be answered in face-to-face interviews. The questionnaire includes this question:

Have you used illegal drugs in the past 12 months?

a) Give one criticism of this question.

b) Give one advantage of using face-to-face interviews to collect data.

Remember — people don't always tell the truth when answering questionnaires.

Q2 The Clena washing machine makers want to find out whether their customers are satisfied with their products. They design a questionnaire which they send by post to all the people who have bought Clena washing machines in the past 12 months. State one problem which the Clena company may have when collecting data in this way.

Q3 A local council wants to find out how they can attract businesses to their area. They design a questionnaire which includes this question:

How many employees at your company watch soap operas?

Give one criticism of this question.

Questions can be either Open or Closed — make sure you know what this means.

Q4 a) Give two reasons for using a pilot study to test a questionnaire.

A cafe owner is trying to find out which drinks his customers prefer. He asks them to complete a questionnaire including this question:

What is your favourite drink?

i)	***Tea***	*ii)*	***Coffee***
iii)	***Fruit squash***	*iv)*	***Other***

52 of the first 100 people to answer reply "other".

b) Give one criticism of the question.

c) How could the question be improved?

Q5 The Milko chocolate company use the following question to find out about the public's taste in chocolate: ***Do you agree that Milko chocolate is the tastiest around?***

In a pilot study, 74% of people answer yes to the question.

a) Give one reason why this has happened.

b) How would you improve the question?

Q6 A drinks company is trying to profile their customers. They want to find out which age groups to target their marketing at. They use this question as part of a questionnaire:

How old are you?

i)	***Under 18***	*ii)*	***18 to 30***	*iii)*	***30 to 40***
iv)	***40 to 60***	*v)*	***over 60***		

a) Give one criticism of this question.

b) How would you improve this question?

Questions on Problems with Question Types

Think hard about the questions you use in a questionnaire, or it'll all go terribly wrong, and as you sob gently over your results, you'll wish you'd listened to me...

Q1 A environmental pressure group is researching attitudes to a proposed bypass around Broughton. The bypass cuts through the Broughton Downs beauty spot. They survey the residents of Broughton using a questionnaire that includes these questions:

Do you think Broughton Downs is beautiful?

Did you know that Broughton Downs will be destroyed when the bypass is built?

Do you agree or disagree with the proposed bypass?

Give one criticism of the group of questions.

Q2 Stanley is researching the use of the school canteen.
He asks this question to a sample of students at the school:

How often do you use the canteen? Tick one of the boxes.

Very often ☐ *Quite often* ☐ *Not very often* ☐ *Never* ☐

a) Give one criticism of Stanley's question.

b) Write a question that Stanley could use to find out how often students at his school use the canteen.

Q3 There is a list of questions below. Say whether each question is open or closed.

a) Where did you go on holiday last year?

b) Do you own a computer?

c) What are your opinions on smoking?

d) Do you think smoking should be banned in all public places?

Q4 Neeta is writing a questionnaire to find out about how students travel to her school.

a) Write one open question that Neeta could use.

b) Write one closed question that Neeta could use.

Q5 Peter compiles a questionnaire on music tastes and sends it to a sample of 100 students at his school. He receives 55 questionnaires back.

a) State one problem that Peter could have with his data.

b) What could Peter do to avoid this problem?

It's a good idea to find out if your questionnaire is any good before using it for real.

Q6 Give two ways in which data from questionnaires can be biased.

Questions on Opinion Scales & Random Response

Opinion scales and random responses are excellent ways of getting the best information from tricky questions — make sure you've learnt how to use them...

AQA only Higher

Q1 Give one advantage of using a question with an opinion scale instead of a yes/no question on a questionnaire.

AQA only Higher

Q2 A sixth-form college is trying to find out its students' opinions on its facilities.

a) Write a question with an opinion scale answer to find out whether the students are satisfied with the choice of books in the library.

b) Write a question with an opinion scale answer to find out whether the students are happy with the standard of the food served in the canteen.

AQA only Higher

Q3 An environmental pressure group wants to survey the people who live in Anclesfield town about their opinions on whether a new landfill site should be created.

They ask the following question: ***Do you agree with the new landfill site?***

Tick the box which applies to you: ***Yes***  ***No*** ☐

a) Give one criticism of this question.

b) Write a question with an opinion scale answer which the environmental group could use to find out opinions on the landfill site.

Higher

Q4 For what types of question might an interviewer use the technique of random response?

Higher

Q5 A youth group leader wants to find out what proportion of the group members smoke cigarettes. He knows that some members will not answer truthfully if he asks them whether they smoke cigarettes. Describe how the technique of random response could be used to get the answer to this question.

Higher

Q6 In a study on the diet of secondary school students, a health researcher asks the question:

"Do you eat one or more bars of chocolate every day?"

She knows that some students will not answer this question truthfully, so she asks them to toss a coin. If it shows heads, they tick the yes box, but if it shows tails they have to answer the question.

In a sample of 1000 students, 632 answer yes.

Use these figures to estimate what percentage of the students eat one or more bars of chocolate every day.

Questions on Interviews

Q1 Mr. Flyalot works for a market research company as an interviewer. His wife Mrs. Flyalot runs her own travel agency business. The market research company is carrying out a survey to find out what people look for in a holiday. Give one reason why Mr. Flyalot should not be used to collect this data.

Q2 Say whether each of the questions listed below is more suited for use in a face-to-face interview or in a questionnaire.

a) What is your opinion on eating chocolate in public places?

b) Tick the boxes which describe what you had for breakfast today. You can tick more than one box.

Toast	☐	Cereal	☐	Fruit Juice	☐
Tea or Coffee	☐	Cooked Breakfast	☐	Other	☐

c) Why did you buy a house in this area?

d) What sports do you take part in?

e) Did you travel to work by bus this morning?

Q3 A teen magazine sends out an anonymous questionnaire which includes the following question:

"Have you knowingly broken the law in the last twelve months?"

Give one reason why this question would not be suitable for use in a face-to-face interview.

Q4 a) Give one reason why the question below is more suitable for use in a face-to-face interview than a questionnaire.

"What type of food do you most enjoy when eating out?"

b) Write a question which gives the same information as the question in part a). Your question should be suitable for use in a questionnaire.

Q5 The government is carrying out a survey on income and family expenditure. They consider two methods of collecting data from a widespread sample of households:

Method A: Send a questionnaire out by post to each household, to be returned by post.

Method B: Devise a questionnaire and use it in a face-to-face interview.

a) Give two advantages of method A.

b) Give two advantages of method B.

Questions on Obtaining Data

When you plan an experiment, make sure you know what the variables are — then you can design a fair test, where everything's constant except the bits you're interested in.

Q1 Cleo decides to do a 20-kilometre cycle ride every day for 20 days to improve her fitness. For each trip she uses a heart rate monitor to record her average heart rate and a stopwatch to record the time. Cleo wants to determine how her fitness changes during these 20 days.

a) Describe a suitable way for Cleo to plan her cycling so that she can use the monitor and stopwatch to assess her changing fitness.

b) For your answer to part (a), what is the response variable?

c) Describe two variables which Cleo should keep constant for her results to be meaningful. Explain your reasoning.

d) Describe one variable which Cleo would like to keep constant but which in practice cannot be.

Extraneous variables are ones that you're not investigating — it's important that these ones stay constant during the test.

Q2 Photographic film is developed by immersing it in a chemical solution. The time it takes depends on the temperature of the solution and can be worked out using the graph below.

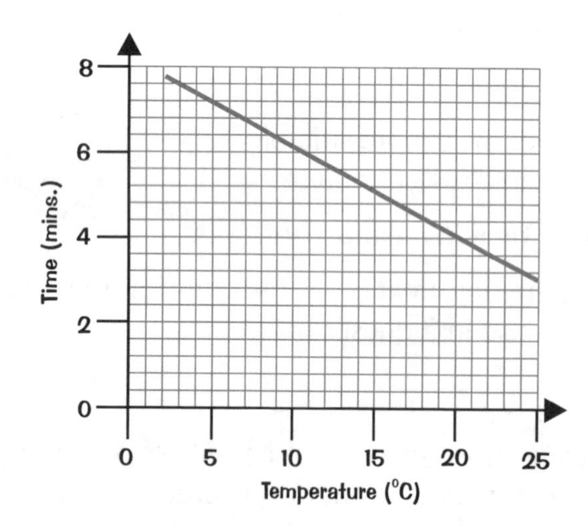

Remember — an independent variable is the same thing as an explanatory variable, and a dependent variable is the same as a response variable.

a) A solution at 20 °C takes 4 minutes to develop a film. How long to the nearest minute would a similar film take to develop at (i) 25 °C (ii) 16 °C?

b) State whether time and temperature are dependent or independent variables.

c) Give one variable which must be kept constant for the graph to be useful when developing films.

Questions on Obtaining Data

Control groups are really important for testing your hypotheses — you'll need to know what they are and how to use them for this page...

Q3 A possible cure for the common cold is to be tested on 100 volunteers, who have all been infected with the same cold virus for the experiment.

The potential cure is in the form of a single tablet to be taken daily, and there are 730 tablets available for the experiment, which will last 14 days.

a) How many of the volunteers would you give tablets to for the two weeks of your experiment?

b) What would you do with the remaining volunteers?

c) How would you ensure that the volunteers were all treated alike?

d) State two variables which you would seek to keep constant throughout the experiment.

Q4 A printer manufacturer wants to test its new black ink cartridge against a similar one sold by a competitor. The company prints the same page of text many times over and records how many pages are printed before the cartridge runs out. It then repeats the test using the competitor's cartridge.

a) Identify the explanatory and response variables for this experiment.

Higher → **b)** You are asked to design the experiment for the manufacturer. Describe three important aspects of your experiment which would ensure that the company gets fair results from the tests.

Don't forget that matched pairs are used to test two groups that are identical except for one variable.

Higher → **Q5** The government wants to know how much subject knowledge gets forgotten by students over the summer holidays. A fair test is needed to test a sample of students both before and after their holidays.

a) Devise a test to investigate this. How would you ensure that the test was fair?

b) State the explanatory variable from your test.

c) Which variable in your test is the response variable?

The table below contains before-and-after results for a group of 10 students.

Score before	88	57	69	58	74	73	59	63	60	76
Score after	75	52	58	50	65	66	48	56	54	62

d) How would you use these results to make a comparison between the students' knowledge before and after the summer holidays?

e) What conclusions could you draw from the experiment?

Questions on Surveys & Capture/Recapture

When you use the capture and recapture method to estimate population sizes, you've got to be careful about the sample you use — make sure you know all about it...

Q1 A large lake in a public park needs to be emptied and dredged of silt. The council want to find out how many fish live in the lake.

One afternoon volunteers net and mark 112 fish, then safely return them to the lake. A few minutes later, the volunteers net 30 fish and find that 12 of these are marked.

a) What assumptions do you have to make to use the capture / recapture method for finding out population sizes?

b) Calculate the number of fish that the council might expect to be in the lake. Show your working clearly.

c) Why might the council have a misleading total using this method?

Q2 An environmental health officer wants to know how many rats and mice live in London's sewers. On one visit, she captures and tags 70 rats and 30 mice before setting them free. The following visit she captures 50 rats and 50 mice and finds that 2 rats and 3 mice are tagged.

a) How many rats would the environmental health officer predict live in the sewers?

b) How many mice can she expect there to be?

c) State two things she should do to make sure that the population survey estimates are as reliable as possible.

Q3 Below is a list of populations:

i) Flies in a field	iv) Trees in a wood
ii) Sheep in a field	v) Bacteria in a Petri dish
iii) Tadpoles in a pond	

a) For each population, state whether capture / recapture could be used to estimate the population sizes.

b) If capture / recapture can't be used for any of the populations, state the reasons why.

Questions on Simulation

Q1 A random number table needs to be generated for a simulation. Each number is made by using the first three significant figures of a random number produced on a calculator *(Ran# on mine)*. The first two random numbers have been put in the table for you.

a) Copy and complete the table below, using your calculator to generate the remaining random numbers.

639	225								

Random number tables are used to simulate random events happening.

b) When spun, a fair coin has an equal chance of showing heads or tails. Design a method of using the completed random number table to simulate spinning a fair coin. Explain your method carefully.

Q2 The 5-digit random number table below is to be used to simulate rolling two fair dice simultaneously. The simulated scores from each dice are to be added together for each 'roll'.

43522	41668	32142	20665	31985
76250	77071	34216	93946	34608
24155	65806	54443	13510	31415

Mel decides to use the first digit of each random number to represent the first dice, and the second digit to represent the other dice. She ignores the random number altogether if either digit is a seven or more.

a) There is another digit which makes Mel ignore a random number. What is it?

b) Copy and complete the table below for 10 simulated rolls of the pair of dice, using Mel's method.

1st Dice	4									
2nd Dice	3									
TOTAL	7									

c) Mel looks at the rolls in her table and sees that there are six threes, so states that 3 is the most likely roll. Comment on her conclusion.

d) Mel also notices that 7 is the most common total. Comment on this conclusion.

Phew, the end of the section. By now you should be a virtuoso of data collection techniques, so bring on the data analysis...

Questions on Frequency Tables

Frequency tables are bound to come up in the exam and are a good place to pick up some REALLY EASY MARKS — so make sure you know this stuff.

Q1 Zoe plays pool in her youth club. She writes down how many of her pool balls are left on the table at the end of every game. Here are her results:

3, 0, 7, 2, 1, 3, 1, 6, 4, 0, 5, 2, 0, 7, 3, 2, 1, 1, 0, 0, 0.

a) Copy and complete the frequency table below for Zoe's data.

Pool Balls	0	1	2	3	4	5	6	7
Tally								
Frequency								

b) How many games does Zoe record in total?

c) To win a game, Zoe must pot all of her seven balls and the black. Is it possible to tell from the frequency table how many games Zoe won?

Q2 Fiona records how many birds she sees visiting her bird table each day. Here are Fiona's results:

3, 8, 5, 7, 4, 3, 2, 6, 4, 7, 5, 4, 4, 6.

a) On how many days did Fiona record the number of birds?

b) What was the highest number of birds that Fiona saw visit her bird table in one day?

c) Copy and complete this frequency table for Fiona's data.

Number of birds	0	1	2	3	4	5	6	7	8	9
Tally										
Frequency										

d) What number of birds did Fiona see most often?

Questions on Grouped Frequency Tables

Grouped frequency tables are defined by classes and there are a few tricky things you need to know — Class Widths, Class Boundaries and Mid-Interval Values... So learn them all and you'll feel as happy as a kipper in a tie shop.

Q1 A group of Year 10 pupils are given 'yellis' scores. These help predict how well they will do in their GCSEs. Their teacher lists them below:

5.1, 6.2, 7.9, 6.0, 4.1, 5.6, 7.0, 6.8, 6.7, 5.3, 6.3, 7.2, 5.0, 5.8, 3.1.

a) Copy and complete this grouped frequency table:

Score (s)	Tally	Frequency
$3.0 < s \le 3.5$		
$3.5 < s \le 4.0$		
$4.0 < s \le 4.5$		
$4.5 < s \le 5.0$		
$5.0 < s \le 5.5$		
$5.5 < s \le 6.0$		
$6.0 < s \le 6.5$		
$6.5 < s \le 7.0$		
$s > 7.0$		

b) The teacher summarises this data in a frequency table with only four classes. Copy and complete the following table to show this.

Score (s)	Tally	Frequency
$3.0 < s \le 4.0$		
$4.0 < s \le 5.0$		
$5.0 < s \le 6.0$		
$s > 6.0$		

c) Why might it be better to use this second table instead of the first?

d) What might be wrong with the way the teacher has simplified the original table?

Q2 A United Nations report on global economies contains the following data about Brazil's national growth rate:

Growth Rate (average % every year)

	1965-1980	1980-1990	1990-1994
Brazil	8.8	2.7	2.2

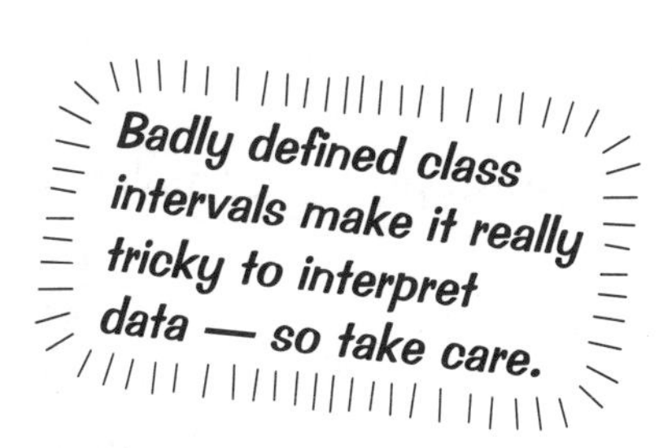

Alex looks at the table and thinks the year classes are badly chosen. Suggest why he thinks they are bad.

Questions on Simplifying and Analysing Data

Q1 Each member of a class of 32 throws the javelin. Their distances are rounded to the nearest metre and summarised in the bar chart below.

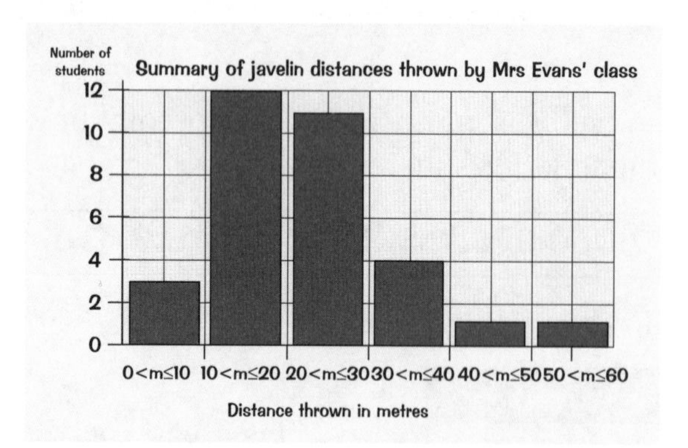

Don't forget — when you've got loads of data, it is probably best to simplify it. This will make the data easier to interpret, but you'll lose some of the original detail.

a) Copy and complete the following table, using data from the graph.

Distance (m):	0<m≤10	10<m≤20	20<m≤30	30<m≤40	40<m≤50	50<m≤60
Frequency	3					

b) Why might rounding to the nearest metre have distorted the data?

c) The table is simplified by using larger class widths for the distances. Copy and complete this new table:

Distance (m)	0<m≤20	20<m≤40	40<m≤60
Frequency			

d) What important details have been lost by this simplification?

Q2 A pet shop owner has kept a record of the number of each type of animal she sold over 4 years:

Animal	2000	2001	2002	2003
Rabbits	68	90	112	120
Rats	30	28	35	36
Guinea Pigs	45	42	30	40
Stick Insects	20	18	10	9
Parrots	4	6	16	12

a) Copy and complete this new table for the total number of animals sold each year:

Year	2000	2001	2002	2003
Total				

b) What does this table show you about the total number of animals sold?

c) Now look back at the original table. What detail has been lost by totalling the data?

Questions on Simplifying and Analysing Data

Q3 This question is about smoking in the UK.

Smoking behaviour among secondary school children by age — 1996

Percentage breakdown of smoking behaviour	Age in years			
	12	13	14	15
Regular smoker	4	10	22	30
Occasional smoker	6	9	9	12
Used to smoke	8	10	14	11
Tried smoking	19	28	22	22
Never smoked	63	43	33	25

Use the table to answer the following questions.

a) What proportion of 12-year-olds have never smoked?

b) What proportion of 15-year-olds regularly smoke?

c) Which of the five categories of smoking behaviour appears to change the least across the ages?

d) Describe the trends in **i)** 'regular' smoking, and **ii)** 'never smoked' behaviours.

Q4 The diagram below shows what people think about the way crime has changed in four separate years.

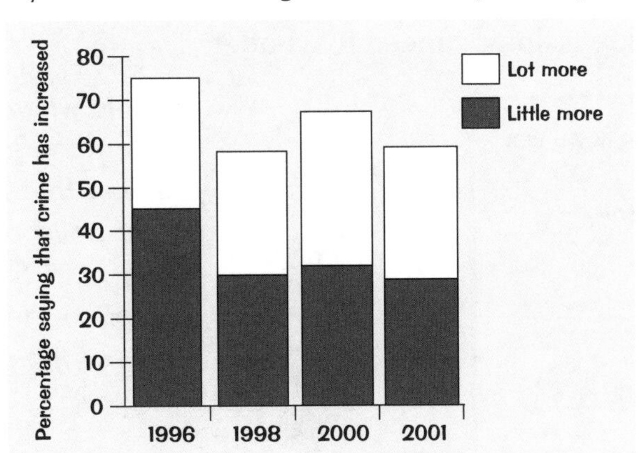

Remember — you're not always given all the information. Think carefully about the data you see in charts and tables, then decide if there's a pattern or trend.

a) What percentage of those asked in 1996 thought that the crime rate had increased a little?

b) What percentage of those asked in 1998 thought that the crime rate had increased a lot?

c) Why do none of the bars total 100%?

d) Georgi says the graph shows that fewer people in 2001 thought that the crime rate had increased, compared to the people asked in 1996. Why might she be wrong?

Questions on Simplifying and Analysing Data

Don't forget, trends are described with terms like 'as x increases, y decreases' — you just have to say what you see to pick up some easy marks in the exam.

Q5 The chart below shows the proportion of each gender that smoke by year.

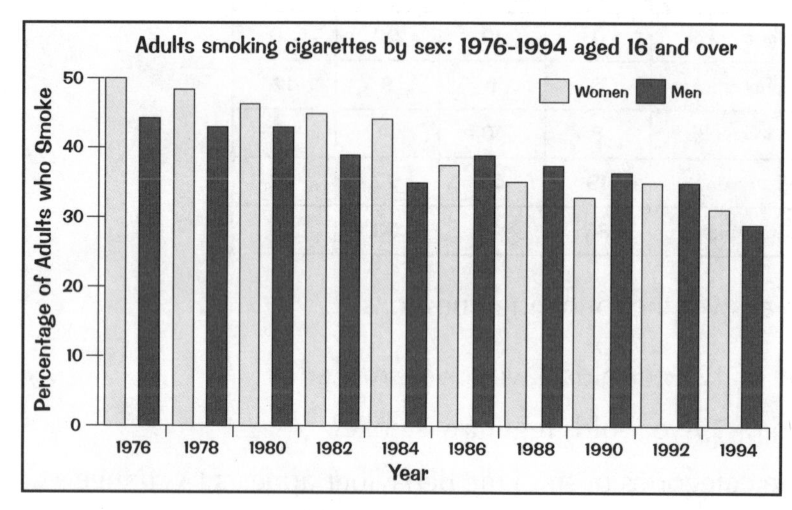

a) Describe the overall trend in smoking habits from 1976 to 1994.

b) What is the difference in the proportion of men and women smoking in 1976?

c) Describe how this difference appears to be changing over the years.

d) Using this chart, estimate what proportion of adults will have smoked in 2000.

This chart shows the death rates due to lung cancer, by gender:

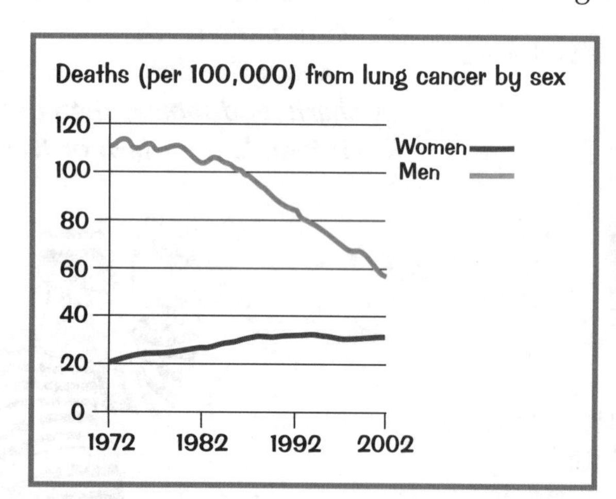

Bias is when someone presents information in a way that backs up their point of view — watch out for this and question the reliability of the data.

A journalist claims that lung cancer deaths during this 30-year period have fallen by around 50% for men whilst at the same time increasing by around 50% for women.

e) Do you agree with the journalist's claims? Explain your reasoning.

Questions on Bar and Pie Charts

Bar charts aren't so bad, but comparative pie charts are nasty little fellas — don't forget that they use the same area per unit of data.

Q1 The graphs below show statistics on marital status for people over 65 years old in 2001.

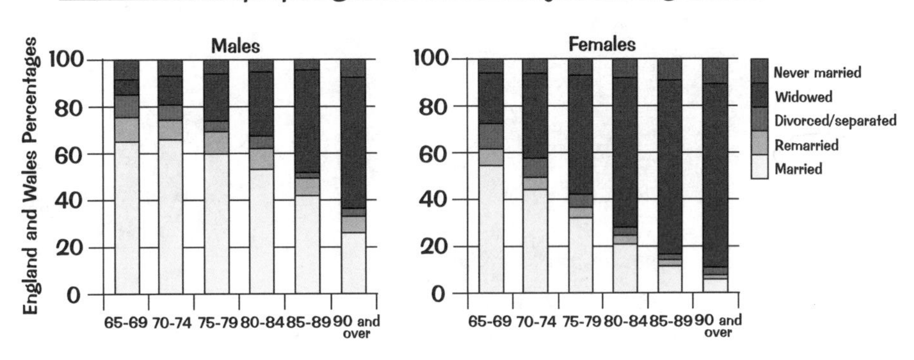

a) What proportion of males aged 65-69 are married?

b) What proportion of females aged 65-69 are married?

c) Jenny thinks that the answers to a) and b) should be the same.
Give two reasons why she might think this.

d) She also works out that the proportion of widowed males aged 90 and over is about 60% and for widowed females of the same age it's about 85%.
Give one reason which would explain such a large difference.

Higher → **Q2** Tom collects data from a Year 10 and a Year 11 class on who is likely to watch the FA Cup final live on TV. His results are shown in the table below.

Will you watch the FA Cup Final live on TV?

	Year 10	Year 11
Definitely	6	4
Very Likely	4	10
Likely	2	6
Unlikely	8	0
No Way	10	0

Compare the results for both year groups using comparative pie charts.
Draw the pie chart for Year 11 with a radius of 3 cm. Show all your workings.

You'll definitely need to know that the Area of a Circle = πr^2 — so make sure you learn it.

Questions on Discrete Data & Frequency Polygons

If there's one thing you need to learn for this page, it's that the Cumulative Frequency tells you the running total of all the frequencies.

Higher

Q1 A manager displays the number of whole days taken off sick by all members of his staff. The data is for a two-week period and is shown in a cumulative frequency graph.

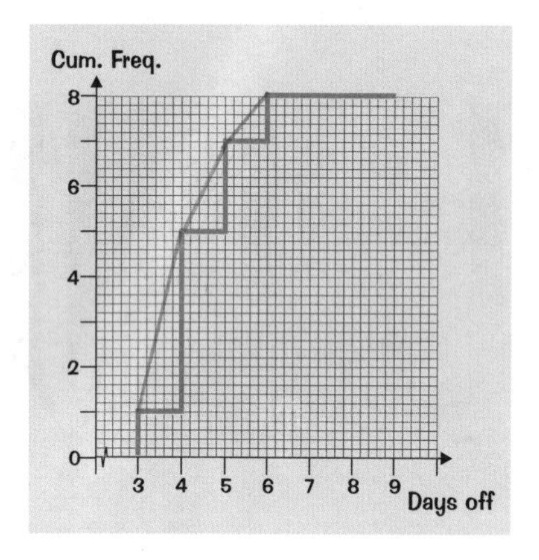

a) How many people work for the manager in this office?

b) His boss doesn't understand the cumulative frequency graph above. On graph paper, draw a line graph to show this data.

Q2 Terry is analysing the number of words in sentences in an English newspaper. Here are his results:

8, 5, 6, 11, 7, 8, 7, 6, 10, 9, 5, 7, 7, 6, 6, 8, 7, 9, 7, 6.

a) Copy and complete the cumulative frequency table below.

No. of Words								
Tally								
Frequency								
Cum Frequency								

Higher

b) On graph paper, draw a cumulative frequency step polygon to show Terry's data.

c) Use the cumulative frequency step polygon to find the median for the data.

Remember — the median is the middle value.

Questions on Other Diagram Types

When the data you are using is continuous, like height, age or speed, join up all the points on your frequency polygon with either a straight line or a nice smooth curve.

Q1 200 athletes take part in a marathon. The times taken (in minutes) for the first 50 athletes to finish the race are shown by the frequency polygon below.

a) How many athletes took between 160 and 165 minutes to finish the race?

b) Find the number of athletes who finished the race in less than 160 minutes.

c) Draw a cumulative frequency graph to show this data.

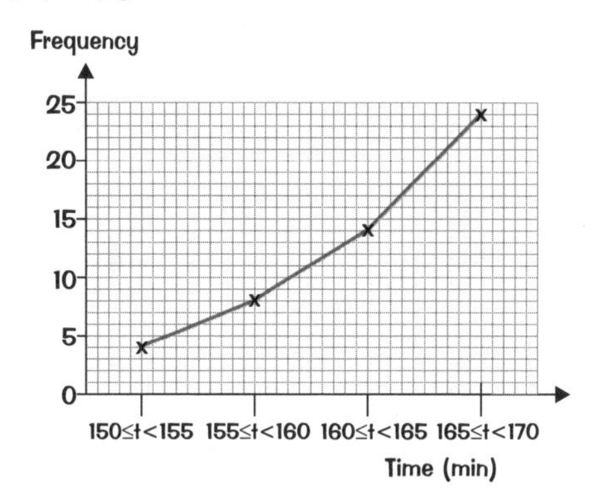

Q2 Jo and Sharon go out together on Friday nights. Each records the amount of money they spend. Jo records her data in the grouped frequency table below.

Jo's Spending

Spending (£)	0≤£<5	5≤£<10	10≤£<15	15≤£<20	20≤£<25
Frequency	1	4	6	2	1

Cumulative frequency is just adding all the frequencies together as you go along.

a) On graph paper, draw a frequency polygon for Jo's data.

Sharon has drawn a cumulative frequency graph of her spending (below).

b) Draw a frequency polygon for Sharon's spending habits (use the same axes as Q2 a).

c) Use Sharon's cumulative frequency graph to find the interquartile range for her data.

d) Copy Sharon's cumulative frequency graph and on the same axes draw the cumulative frequency graph for Jo's data.

e) Using the two cumulative frequency graphs, estimate each girl's median spending to the nearest pound. Who appears to be more reckless with her money?

f) Why might their actual total spending really be within a few pence of each other? Explain your answer.

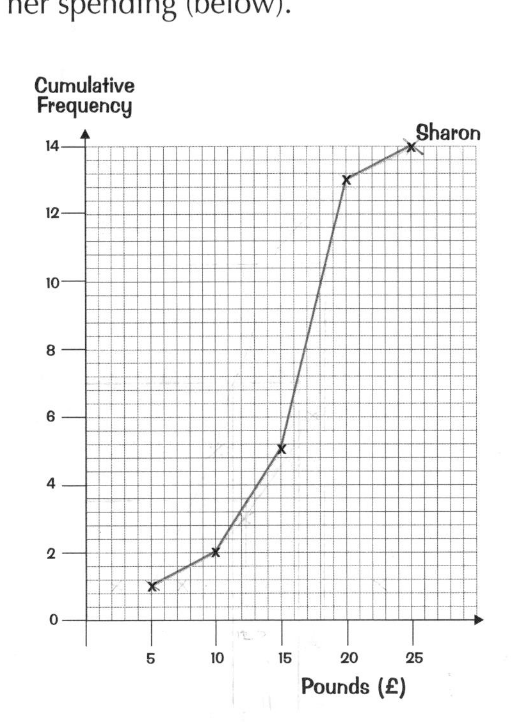

Questions on Other Diagram Types

Q3 These two population pyramids compare the distribution of ages in France and Brazil:

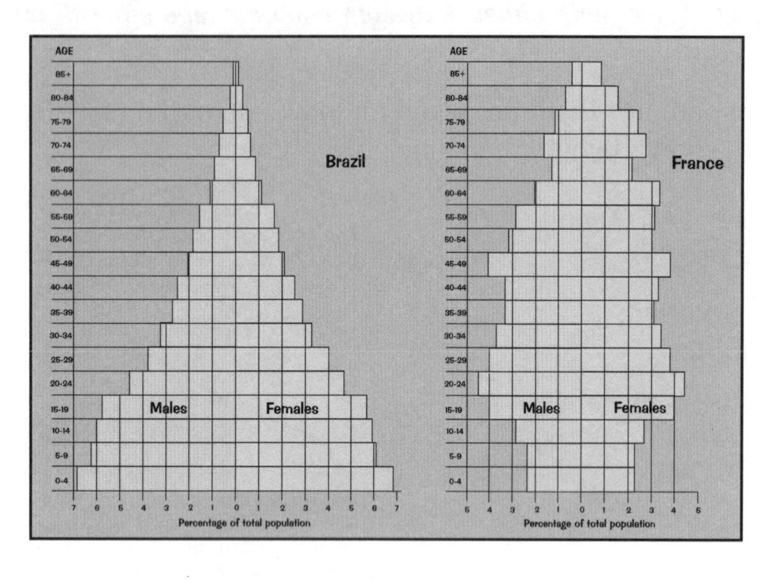

These population pyramids might look a bit scary, but don't worry — just think of them as two bar charts that have been put side by side so you can compare stuff.

a) What percentage of the total population in each country is aged 0-14?

b) Explain why these figures might be different.

c) i) What percentage of males in France are over the age of 70?

ii) What is the equivalent percentage for females?

d) Explain why there is a difference between the proportions of French men and women over the age of 70.

e) What does France's pyramid indicate about the birth rate in recent years?

Higher → **Q4** Michael conducts a survey of cars passing in one direction along his local high street on a weekday. The table below shows his results:

Time, t	0800≤t<0900	0900≤t<1200	1200≤t<1400	1400≤t<1530
Cars, n	100	90	80	75

a) Draw a histogram to represent the data. Show all your workings.

Michael then counts the number of cars from 1530 to 1600 and draws a bar on his histogram for this interval with a frequency density of 150 cars/hr.

b) Calculate the rate of cars passing per minute between 1530 and 1600.

Behold — here is the key to all histogram questions...
Frequency density = Frequency ÷ Class Width

Questions on Stem & Leaf Diagrams and Shading Maps

A Choropleth map is the fancy name for a shaded map — learn this name and you won't get tripped up by a question that asks you to make one.

Q1 The government publishes a report on the UK's economy that contains these two maps:

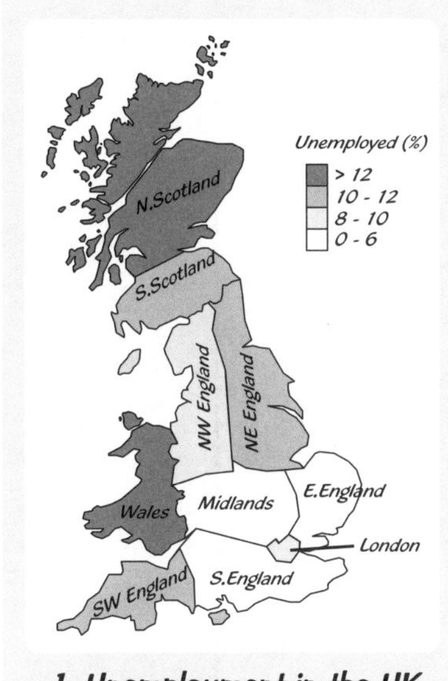

1. Unemployment in the UK

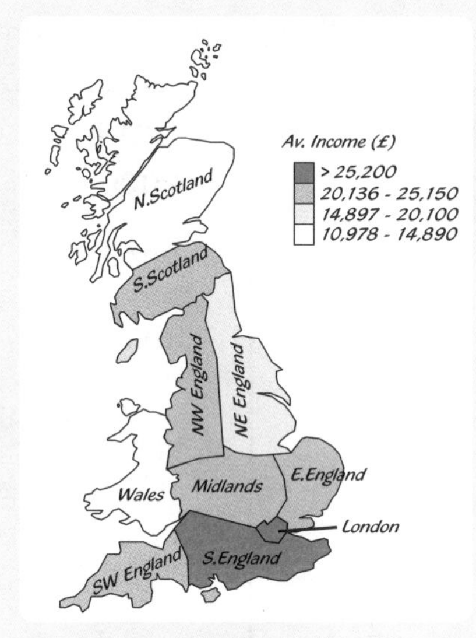

2. Average income in the UK

a) What is the unemployment rate in the north-west of England?

b) What is the average income in the south-west of England?

c) Which region has both the same unemployment and income characteristics as northern Scotland?

d) What do the two maps suggest about unemployment and income characteristics in the south-east of England?

e) One of the regions has an unemployment rate of 11% and an average income of £17k. Which region is it?

f) Comment on the classes used in both keys.

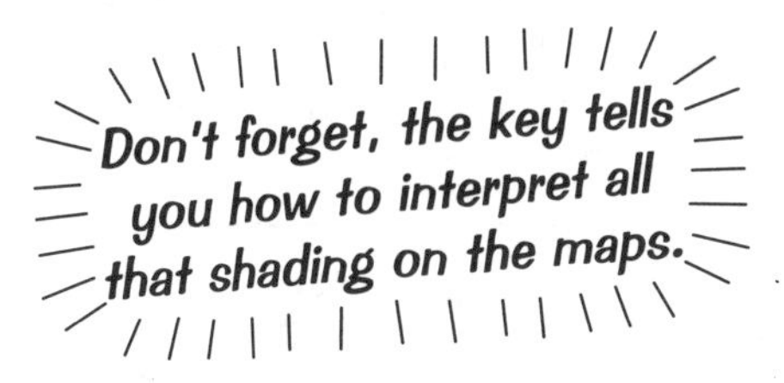

Q2 Jack is training his racing snail for the Mollusc World Championship 50 cm sprint. He records the training times to the nearest second in the list below:

48, 44, 37, 66, 70, 52, 31, 50, 45, 52, 45, 43, 32, 45, 59, 61

a) Construct a stem and leaf diagram to show Jack's data.

b) What is the modal time?

c) What is the range of the times?

Questions on Transforming Data

No nice shaded maps on this page, but there is a tricky little pie chart to get you thinking — make sure you brush up on angles in circles for that one...

Q1 A newspaper article about redundancies at a local company includes the graph below. It shows the fall in the number of employees at a company over time.

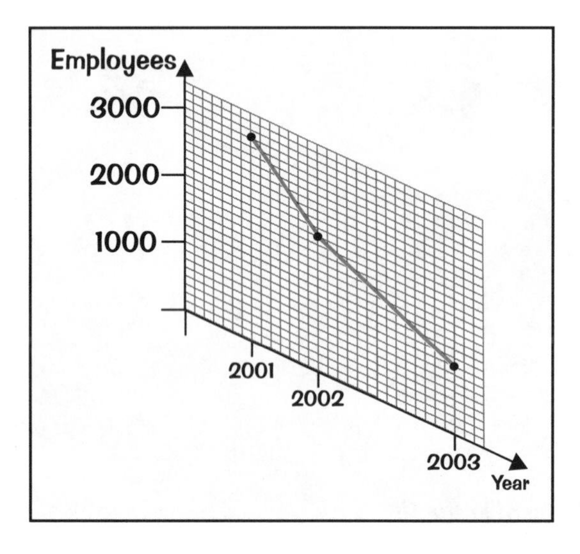

Kirsty uses this newspaper article in a business studies project, but realises that the graph is misleading.

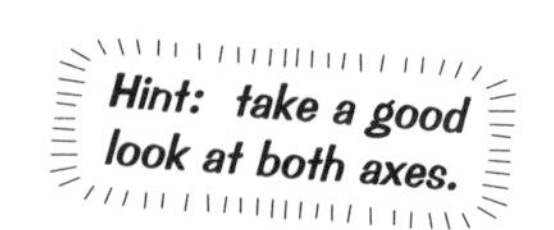

a) On graph paper, draw a line graph that correctly shows the data.

b) Describe the rate of decline in employees at this company over time.

Q2 This bar chart shows the number of sweets of different colours in a large packet. Transform this data into a pie chart. Show all of your workings.

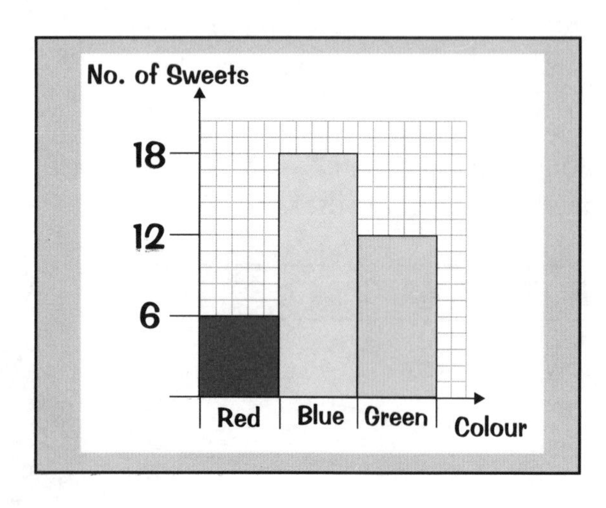

Here are three things you MUST LEARN about circles so that you can answer pie chart questions:

1. ***the angle subtended by a circle at its centre is 360°.***
2. ***the Area of a circle = πr^2.***
3. ***Circles are round.***

Questions on Frequency Distributions

Examiners love to ask questions about frequency distributions to do with the skew, mode, median and range — so go into your exam knowing what these terms mean... learn them now.

Q1 Two spinners are spun and the scores on each added together. This is done 30 times for three different pairs of spinners. The results are shown in the graphs below.

For each pair of spinners below, describe:

i) the skew of the distribution.

ii) the range of total scores.

iii) the modal score.

iv) the median score.

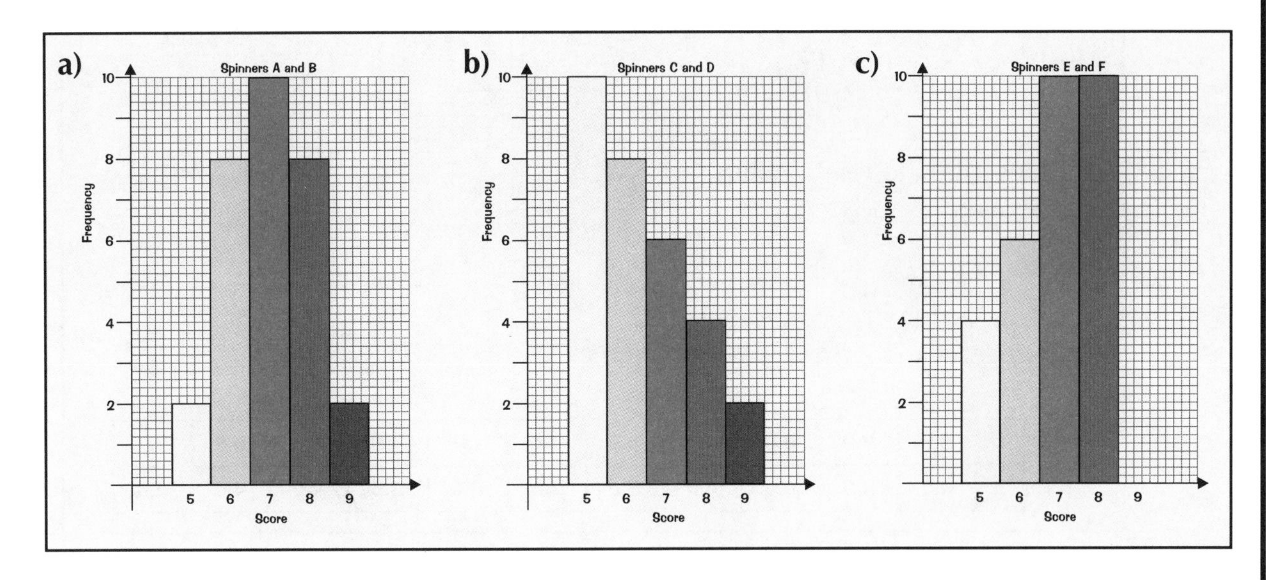

Q2 The number of people in their 50s, 60s and 70s in three villages, A, B and C, are shown in the bar frequency graph below.

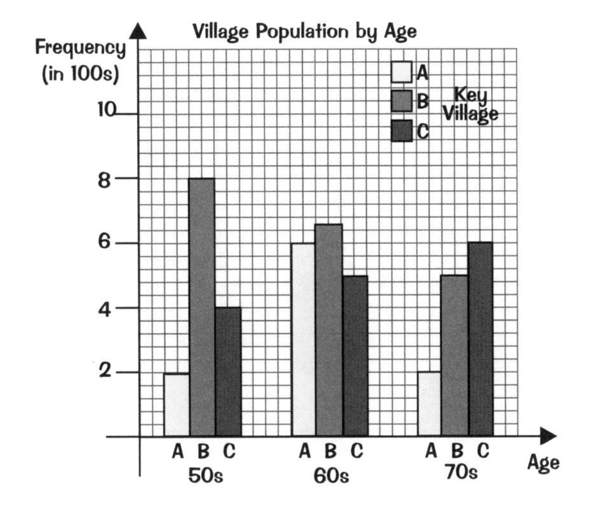

a) Calculate the number of people from each village in the survey.

b) Which village has the highest proportion of people who are in their 60s?

c) Describe the age distributions for each village.

Questions on Scatter Diagrams & Line Graphs

Scatter graphs might look a bit random at first, but there might actually be a relationship in there — which can be described using the 'line of best fit'.

Q1 The scatter graph shows the data from the table below. Four points have yet to be plotted.

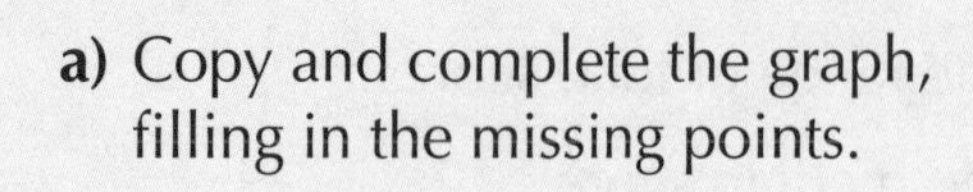

a) Copy and complete the graph, filling in the missing points.

b) Draw on a line of best fit.

c) Describe the relationship between x and y.

d) What value of y would you expect if x is 2.5?

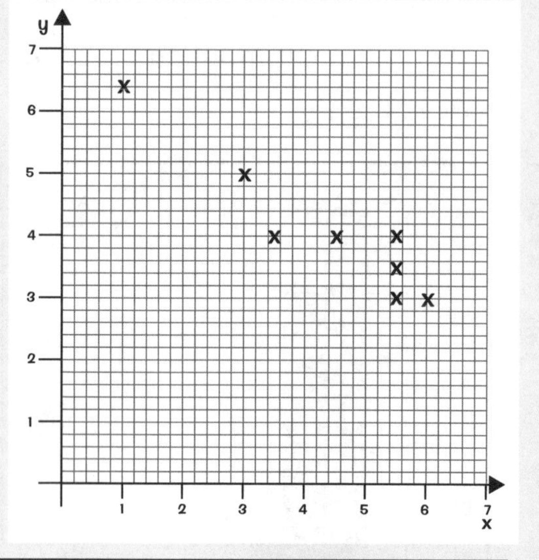

x	3.5	3.0	6.0	4.0	5.5	2.0	1.0	5.5	4.5	5.5	7.0
y	4.0	5.0	3.0	4.0	3.0	7.0	6.5	3.5	4.0	4.0	2.0

Q2 What relationships would you expect to see between the pairs of variables given below? Copy the axes and sketch the lines of best fit that show these relationships.

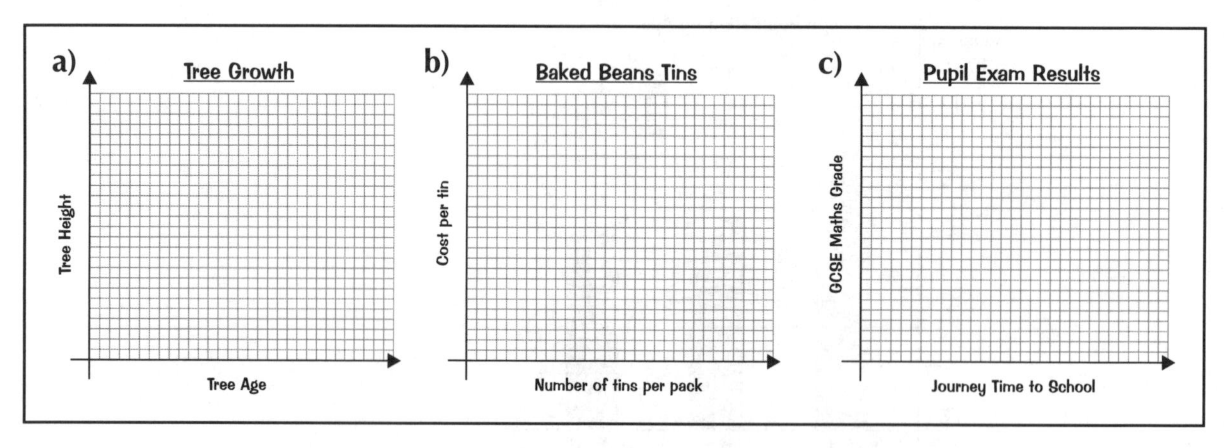

Remember — Correlations between variables can be positive, negative or not exist at all.

Questions on More Diagram Types

Diagrams comparing two sets of data can be very misleading sometimes — make sure you learn about Scale Factors for this lot.

Higher

Q1 Fred practises hitting a hockey ball at a target net. In each practice, he takes 100 shots. In the first practice, he hit the target 40 times. In the second practice, he hit the target 80 times. Fred draws 5 different diagrams to show how his shooting has improved.

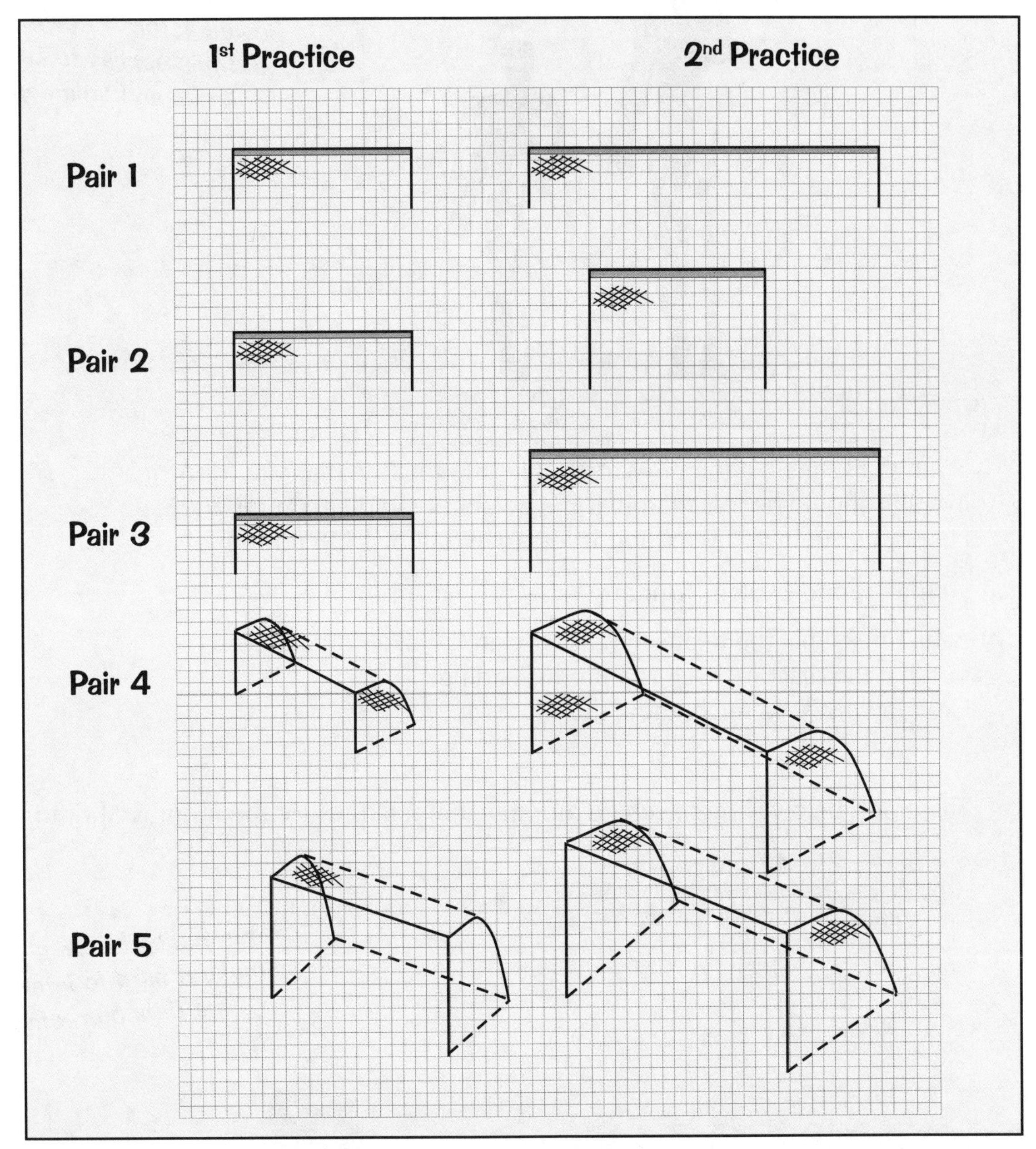

a) Which of the diagrams correctly show Fred's improved shooting? Which are misleading?

b) Explain why the diagrams which are misleading are not correct representations of Fred's practice results.

Higher

Q2 Amy's teacher reckons that Amy chats three times as much as Kayleigh.
She draws a circle of radius 3 cm to represent Kayleigh's chatting.
What diameter circle should she draw to represent Amy's chatting? Show your workings.

Questions on Problems with Diagrams

Higher → **Q1** This diagram shows the populations of Asia and Africa in 1994 and predictions for both populations in 2025.

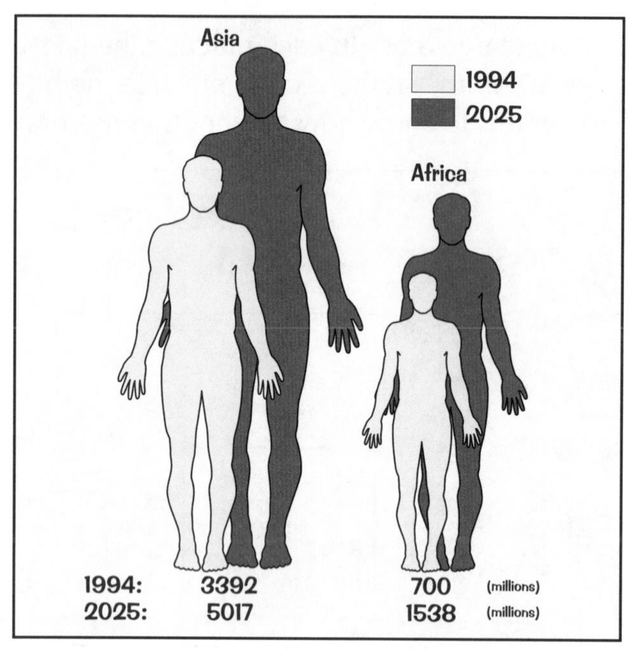

Don't forget this useful rule: Scale Factor = New ÷ Old ...and this applies to Lengths, Areas and Volumes.

Brian thinks the diagram is wrong. He says that the diagram for Africa in 1994 should be less than half the height of the diagram for 2025. He points out that 700 million is less than half of 1538 million.

a) Is Brian right? Explain your answer.

b) Asha thinks that the relative areas used in the diagram are correct but that the diagram itself is a bit misleading. Explain why Asha might think this.

Q2 The graph below shows average monthly temperatures for the months April to August.

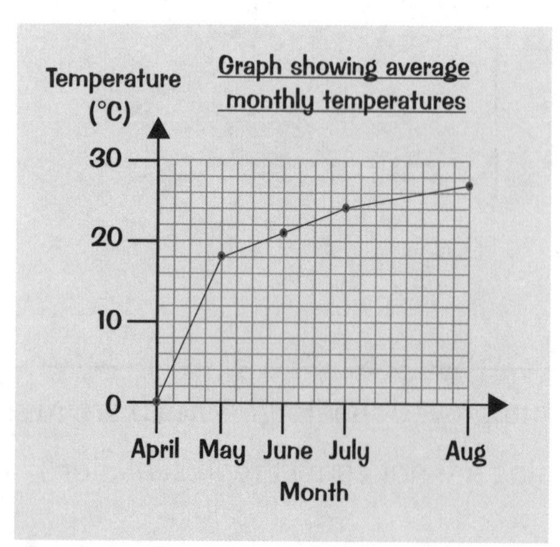

a) Jane thinks that the temperature for April has been plotted incorrectly. Do you agree? Explain your answer.

b) The x-axis is unevenly scaled. What effect does this have on the graph?

Questions on Spotting Errors in Diagrams

Diagrams like the one in Q1 are frequently used to represent data in newspapers, textbooks and your EXAM — just make sure you understand how to use the Key and you'll be laughing when a question like this comes up.

Q1 The diagram shows information about two large regions of the world.
Information includes populations, income, etc.
The key shows the value of each symbol.

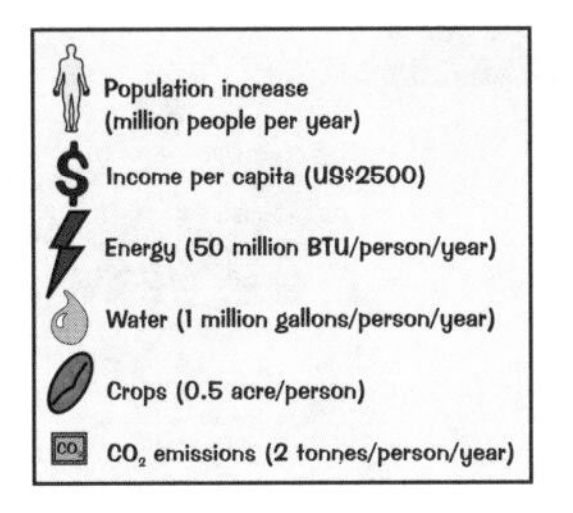

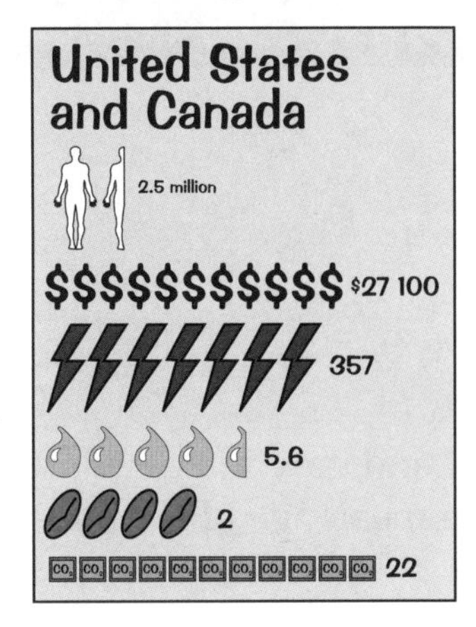

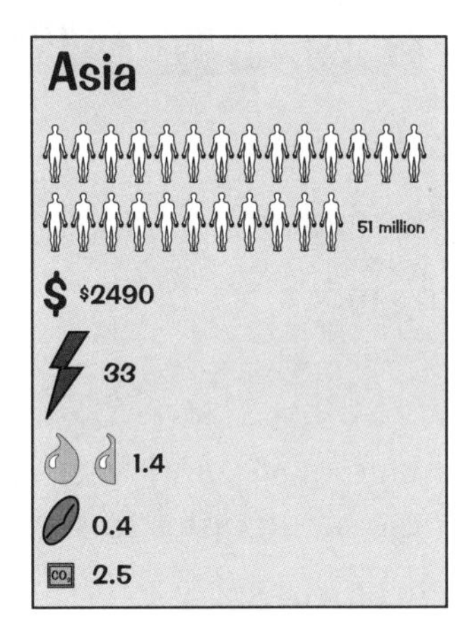

a) What name best describes this type of diagram?

b) How would you represent 5 tonnes/person/year of CO_2 emissions on the diagram?

c) One lightning symbol represents 50 million units of energy (BTU/person/year).
Do the energy diagrams appear to correctly show the energy data given?
Explain your answer.

d) Karl thinks that there is one mistake in each of the population increase diagrams.
What has Karl noticed?

Q2 This graph shows the mean pocket money received by each year group in a school:

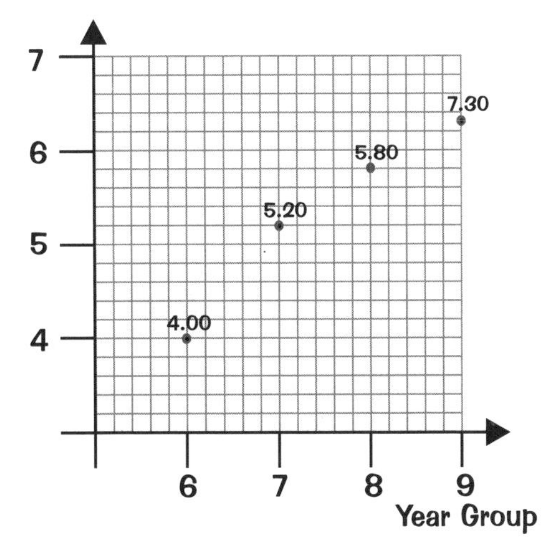

Always be critical of the data you see — don't just assume it's right because it's in the paper.

a) Identify three errors in the graph.

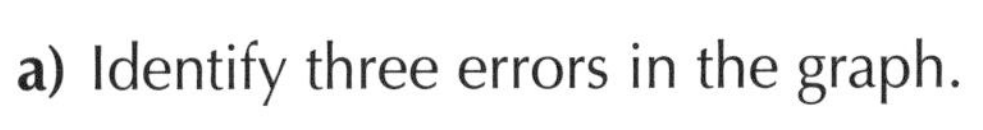

b) Redraw the graph to show the information in a way which is not misleading or inaccurate.

Questions on Mean, Median and Mode

Make sure you know the difference between MEAN, MEDIAN AND MODE, and how to work them out. You've got three pages of practice here, so get stuck in.

Q1 These are the heights in metres of twenty Year 11 students:

1.65	1.48	1.82	1.63	1.68	1.52	1.65	1.54	1.65	1.50
1.53	1.80	1.77	1.54	1.55	1.70	1.68	1.65	1.72	1.76

a) Calculate the mean.

b) What is the median?

c) What is the mode?

Q2 The mean age of Mr. and Mrs. Short and their three children is 15.
When Uncle Sam comes to stay, the mean age of the household rises to 18.

How old is Uncle Sam?

Q3 The times taken by 12 members of the Hackney Harriers to run the London marathon are recorded below:

2hr31m	2hr45m	2hr38m	2hr35m	2hr50m	2hr54m
2hr28m	2hr35m	2hr42m	2hr35m	2hr48m	2hr39m

a) Calculate the mean. *You may find it easier to take away a suitably chosen value first, but don't forget to add it back in again.*

b) Work out the median.

AQA only Higher → **Q4** Susan was copying out some data for her statistics coursework, but she couldn't read two out of six numbers. The remaining four numbers were:

7 4 6 8

She knew that the mean and the median were both equal to six.
What were the two missing numbers?

Higher → **Q5** A mathematics exam consists of two question papers and a piece of coursework. The papers contribute 40% each to the final result and the coursework counts for the remaining 20%. What is a student's final percentage if she scores 50%, 65% and 45% for the two papers and the coursework respectively?

Questions on Mean, Median and Mode

Q6 Every time Roger plays golf he keeps a record of his score on the first hole. The table below shows his last 120 scores.

Score	3	4	5	6	7	8
Frequency	2	15	38	34	23	8

a) Calculate the mean.

b) In which group is the median?

c) What is the modal group?

Q7 One of the competitions at a fête involved guessing the number of sweets in a jar. The guesses were recorded and tabulated:

Guess	51-70	71-90	91-110	111-130	131-150	151-170
Frequency	2	15	28	24	18	8

a) Calculate an estimate for the mean.

b) Why is the answer to part a) only an estimate?

c) In which group is the median?

d) What is the modal group?

Don't forget the difference between <u>discrete</u> data and <u>continuous</u> data.

Q8 Eric and Bill played a darts match. A breakdown of their scores is shown in the table:

Score	1-30	31-60	61-90	91-120	121-150	151-180
Eric	2	34	32	5	3	1
Bill	2	47	18	6	2	1

a) Which of the mean, median and mode should you use to decide who probably won?

b) Who do you think won, and why?

Q9 Susan runs a 'Fat Club' and made notes for her 40 clients. Ten weighed between 70 and 90 kilograms, 16 weighed between 90 and 110 kilograms and 14 weighed between 110 and 140 kilos.

a) What is an estimate for their mean weight?

b) Which is the modal group?

c) In which group is the median weight?

Questions on Mean, Median and Mode

Q10 A manufacturer tested the lifetime of a particular type of light bulb so that he could confidently state how many hours they lasted. The results for eight such light bulbs are as follows:

3090	2400	2010	2520	90	2620	2800	2550

a) Which average should he use to justify his statement?

b) Which average would be the least useful, and why?

c) What should the manufacturer do to be more sure of his statement?

Q11 What one main advantage does the mode have over the mean and the median?

Higher

Q12 State the most appropriate average (mean, median or mode) for working out each of the following:

a) A cricketer's batting average.

b) The most popular type of music at a school.

c) The average length of tennis rallies in the men's final at Wimbledon.

d) The average number of people attending church on Sunday mornings.

Higher

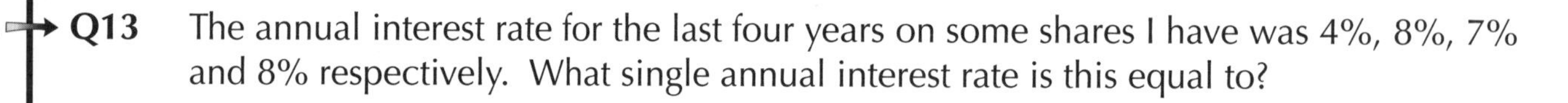

Q13 The annual interest rate for the last four years on some shares I have was 4%, 8%, 7% and 8% respectively. What single annual interest rate is this equal to?

Q14 If over a period of four years you are offered consecutive annual interest rates of 6%, 7%, 8% and 9% or a fixed annual interest rate of 7.5%, which should you take?

Justify your answer.

You need to remember when it's best to use the mean, median and mode — and why...

Questions on Range and Quartiles

Remember to put the data in ascending order before you work out where the quartiles, deciles or percentiles come in a list.

Q1 The following table shows the number of cars parked in a multi-storey car park at midday on each day in December:

690	720	580	590	210	650	640	710	700	750	790	220	790	840	830	820
900	880	480	1000	990	1020	1010	1000	80	240	370	510	460	600	580	

a) What is the range?

b) What is the lower quartile, Q_1?

c) What is the median, Q_2?

d) What is the upper quartile, Q_3?

Quartiles divide the data into 4 equal groups, deciles divide it into 10 equal groups and percentiles divide it into 100 equal groups.

Q2 The weights (in g) of 29 eggs are:

60	72	58	60	68	69	59	72	54	56	65	68	63	70	71
67	64	63	69	62	63	67	59	72	61	66	65	67	70	

a) What is the median, Q_2?

Higher → **b)** Which decile is equivalent to the median?

c) What is the 9th decile, D_9?

Q3 The range of 99 different integers is 98, and the median is 350.

a) What is the lower quartile, Q_1?

Higher → **b)** What is the 4th decile, D_4?

c) What is the 3rd percentile, P_3?

d) Which percentile is the number 399?

Q4 The following data shows the number of appointments not kept at the local doctor's surgery each month for the last eleven months:

38	52	18	25	32	21	42	23	29	37	24

a) What is the upper quartile?

Higher → **b)** What is the 5th decile?

c) What is the 50th percentile?

Questions on Interquartile & Interpercentile Range

Q1 The graph on the right shows the cumulative frequency curve for the height in cm of 200 sunflowers at 8 weeks old.

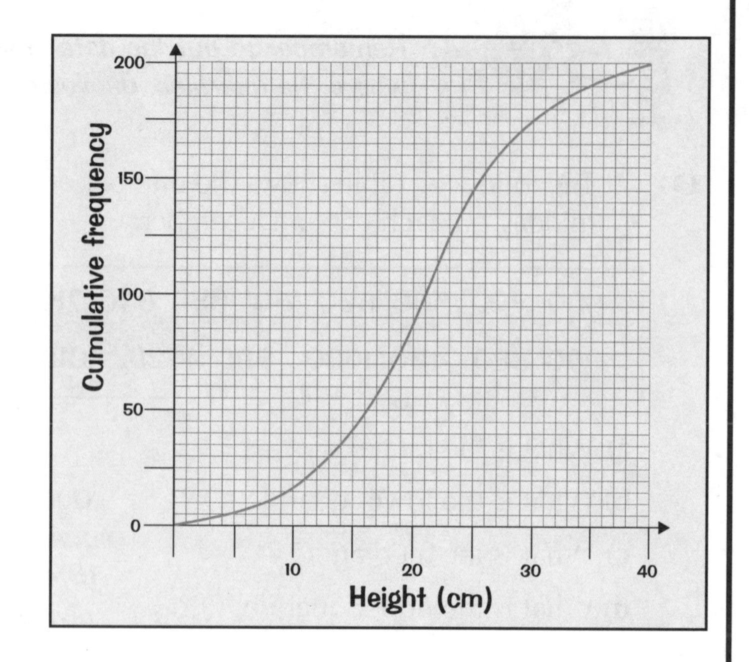

a) What is the interquartile range?

b) What is the 20th percentile?

Higher → **c)** What is the $P_{90} - P_{10}$ percentile range?

Q2 For all the whole numbers from 1 to 399 inclusive:

a) What is the interquartile range?

Higher → **b)** What is the $P_{60} - P_{40}$ percentile range?

The interquartile range tells you the range of the middle 50% of the data.

Q3 The weights (in kg) of a company's employees were taken and recorded in the table below:

Weight (kg)	Freq	Cum freq
w<50	0	0
50≤w<55	3	3
55≤w<60	8	11
60≤w<65	27	38
65≤w<70	32	70
70≤w<75	25	95
75≤w<80	29	124
80≤w<85	35	159
85≤w<90	27	186
90≤w<95	18	204
95≤w<100	6	210

a) Plot the cumulative frequency curve for the data.

b) Use your graph to find:

i) the interquartile range, **ii)** the 30th percentile,

Higher → **iii)** the $P_{70} - P_{30}$ percentile range.

Questions on Variance & Standard Deviation

This page is all Higher stuff, so if you're doing Foundation you can skip straight to the lovely box and whisker plots. Off you go...

Q1 If the variance of a set of data is 1.0404, what is the standard deviation?

Q2 The scores of eight teams at a quiz night are given in the following table:

a) Work out the mean, $\bar{x}$.

b) Copy and complete the table on the right.

c) Using your table, evaluate the standard deviation of the scores.

x	$x-\bar{x}$	$(x-\bar{x})^2$
64		
71		
68		
79		
62		
73		
67		
64		

Q3 The standard deviation of the numbers 1 – 10 inclusive is 2.87.

What is the standard deviation of the numbers 11 – 20 inclusive?

Q4 For a set of data, $\sum x^2 = 3840$, $\bar{x} = 17.4$ and n = 12.

Use this information to calculate the standard deviation.

Q5 A man weighed himself on ten different makes of bathroom scales with the following results in kg:

85.8	85.9	86.0	85.7	85.9
85.8	86.1	86.0	85.8	85.9

a) Calculate the mean weight.

b) Calculate the variance and hence the standard deviation of these weights.

You need to be comfortable using the formulas for variance and standard deviation — but they'll be given to you in the exam.

Questions on Box & Whisker Plots

Hey! Pretty pictures... kind of...

Q1 Draw a box plot using the following information:

Lowest value = 1
Range = 38
Lower quartile = 17
Upper quartile = 28
Median = 24

A box and whisker plot is sometimes just called a box plot.

Q2 The scores of Wrinkly Bottom Cricket Club 1st XI were as follows:

103	2	81	57	14	37	42	25	18	7	0

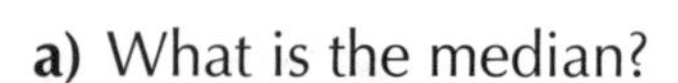

a) What is the median?

b) Work out the interquartile range.

c) Show this data on a box plot.

Q3 This cumulative frequency table shows the lengths of 40 leaves from a young oak tree, measured to the nearest mm.

Draw a cumulative frequency curve of the data and construct a box plot below it.

Length of leaf (mm)	Frequency
≤ 50	4
≤ 60	15
≤ 70	27
≤ 80	35
≤ 90	38
≤ 100	40

Q4 Below is a list of the number of text messages sent by 23 students in one week:

0	8	10	11	12	13	15	17	24	24	25	26
28	32	32	34	37	37	50	55	70	79	88	

a) Draw a box plot to show this data.

Higher

b) If outliers are defined as any values greater than $Q_3 + 1.5(Q_3 - Q_1)$ or less than $Q_1 - 1.5(Q_3 - Q_1)$, identify any outliers in the data above.

AQA only Higher

c) Redraw the box plot taking these outliers into account.

Q_1 = lower quartile
Q_3 = upper quartile

Standardised Scores

Another Higher only page, folks.

Q1 The table below shows the percentages gained in exams for 5 students along with the mean and standard deviation for the whole class.

Subject	Amy	Bob	Carla	David	Edward	Mean	Standard Deviation
History	45	72	61	39	54	47	8
Geography	69	47	52	58	49	51	5.5
Music	75	40	59	52	70	58	6.1
Maths	44	38	49	82	57	55	6.7
English	57	44	53	63	40	54	4.9

a) What is Carla's standardised score for history?

b) What is David's standardised score for music?

c) In which subject did Amy give her best performance?

d) What is Edward's total standardised score?

e) In which subject did Bob give his worst performance?

Don't forget the simple formula for working out standard scores.

Q2 Four people played Scrabble. Their scores are recorded in the table below, along with the mean and standard deviation of all the players' scores for each game.

	Fred	George	Holly	Ivy	Mean	S.D.
Game 1	342	478	246	290	339	87.1
Game 2	501	299	312	288	350	87.6
Game 3	259	320	281	464	331	79.8
Game 4	275	272	510	387	361	97.7

Who was the best Scrabble player?

Q3 Laura and Jane's marks for Information Technology and German are recorded in the table below, along with the mean and standard deviation for the whole class.

	Laura	Jane	Mean	Standard deviation
I.T.	54	48	46	12
German	40	46	44	18

a) Gill noticed that she had the same standardised score for German as Jane had for I.T. What mark did she get?

b) Who did better overall, Laura or Jane?

Questions on Comparing Data Sets

You can use measures of location and spread to compare data sets.

Q1 The four box plots show the spread of mark adjustments made by the team leader to the sample scripts of four examiners, A, B, C and D.

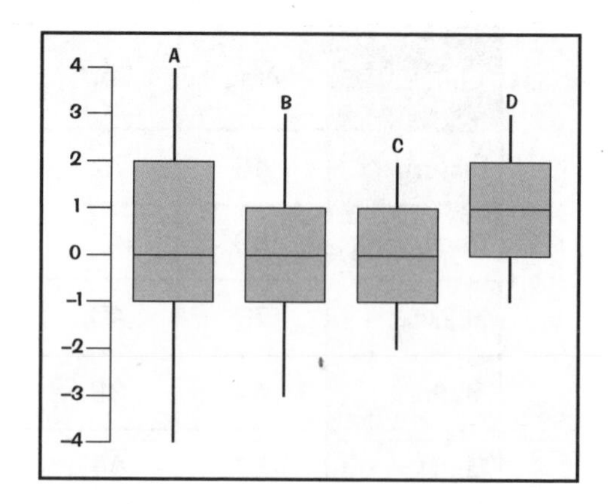

a) Which examiner is the most reliable? Explain your answer.

b) Which examiner is the most unreliable? Give a reason for your answer.

c) What advice would you give to examiner D to improve their marking?

Q2 A summary of two batsmen's scores for a cricket season is shown in the table on the right.

Answer the following questions, giving a reason for each choice.

	A	B
Mean	48	65
Median	47	51
Range	164	130
Standard Deviation	29	24

a) Which batsman was the most consistent?

b) If both batsmen were out for a duck (scored 0) at least once, which batsman had the highest score?

c) Which batsman had the best batting average?

Q3 The cumulative frequency polygons below show the percentage age distribution of three villages, A, B and C.

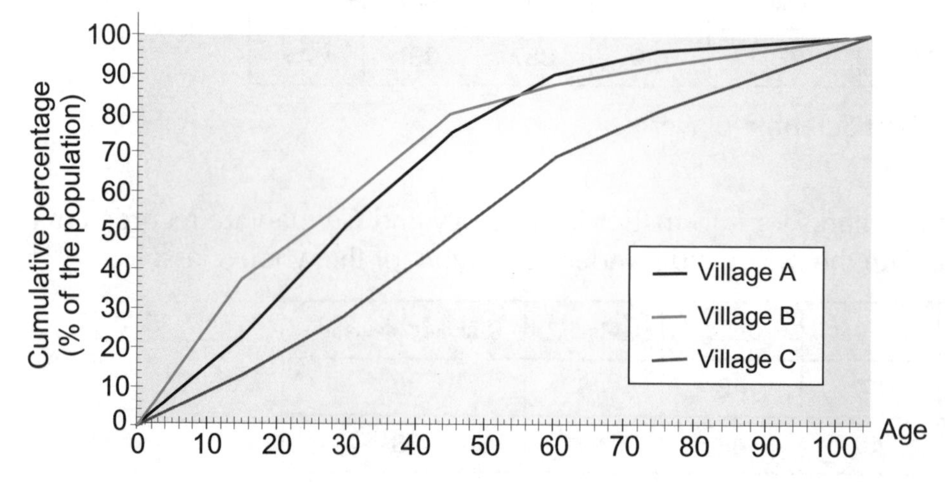

a) One of the villages is recognised as a retirement village. Which one?

b) Jack looks at the cumulative frequency polygons and tells Jenny that there are more children in Village B than in Village A. Can he be sure? Give a reason for your answer.

Questions on Summary Statistics

You've all got to know about index numbers — and if you're doing AQA, crude rates as well. If you're doing Higher, you need to remember the formulas for weighted index numbers and standardised rates. The next three pages give you loads of practice at doing just that — so enjoy. ☺

Q1 Here are the index numbers for the price of a particular model of car since it was launched in the year 2000:

Year	2000	2001	2002	2003
Index	100	108	112	114

a) Which year is the base year?

b) Which year showed the least increase in price from the previous year?

c) If the car first came onto the market for £26 000, what was the price of the car in 2002?

d) If, instead, the price of the car in 2002 was £29 400, what would the car have been sold for in 2003?

Q2 The value of a piece of land has been increasing over the last three years, as shown:

Year	2002	2003	2004
Value (£)	25 000	30 000	32 000

Using 2002 as a base year, calculate the index numbers for the years 2003 and 2004.

Higher → **Q3** Some of the prices (in £) and chain base index numbers for a product over the last four years are shown in the table below.

Year	2001	2002	2003	2004
Price (£)	750	825	858	
Index number	100			95

a) Copy and complete the table.

b) Using 2001 as the base year, calculate the index number for 2004.

Questions on Summary Statistics

Higher

Q4 The makers of a brand of Yorkshire pudding use a batter mix with the following main ingredients:

Milk:	15 litres
Eggs:	100
Flour:	6 kg

The company wants to calculate a weighted index number for the ingredients to help them work out what to charge for their Yorkshire puddings.
The prices for 2003 and 2004, along with two of the weights, are shown below.

	2003	2004	Weight
Milk (per litre)	£0.58	£0.66	15
Eggs (per box of ten)	£1.44	£1.55	
Flour (per kg)	£1.30	£1.45	6

a) What is the appropriate weight for the eggs?

b) Calculate the weighted index number for:

i) the milk

ii) the eggs

iii) the flour.

You need to remember the nice and simple formula for the weighted index number.

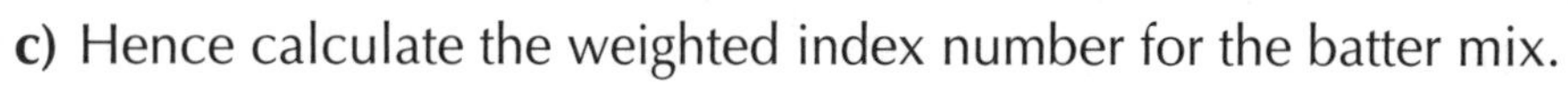

c) Hence calculate the weighted index number for the batter mix.

d) What does this say about the cost in 2004 compared to that in 2003?

AQA only

Q5 Last year the number of deaths in Wentwell was 432.
If Wentwell had a population of 28 600, what was the crude death rate last year?

The crude birth rate is the number of births per thousand of the population.

AQA only

Q6 The crude birth rate in Bournville in 2003 was 21.4.
If the population in 2003 was 15 000, how many babies were born that year?

Questions on Summary Statistics

All the rest of this is AQA Higher now, so you can skip it if you're doing Foundation or Edexcel.

Q7 A breakdown of the numbers of births in Hadham by average age of parents in 2002 is tabulated below.

Age Group	Population	Number of births	Standard population
0-15	460	4	14
16-30	500	82	30
31-50	490	34	35
51+	630	6	21

a) What was the standardised birth rate for Hadham in 2002?

b) If the data was refined to include women only, would the standardised birth rate change? (NB assume that there are equal numbers of males and females in the population.)

c) If all the standard population weights were doubled, would the birth rate change?

Q8 A car insurance company wanted to reassess their rates for drivers to take gender into consideration. [This question assumes there are equal numbers of men and women in the driving population.]

Age Group	Gender	Number insured	Number of claims	Standard population
17-24	Male	20 200	510	28
	Female	30 800	690	
25-59	Male	165 100	3720	54
	Female	155 500	3010	
60+	Male	17 400	850	18
	Female	18 800	950	

By working out the standardised claim rates, decide whether there should be a better deal for female drivers than male drivers.

Q9 An accident insurance company wants to know whether they should insure firemen for more or less than policemen. They know that the standardised rate of claims for a policeman is 15.7. What do they need to know to calculate the standardised rate of claims for a fireman?

Questions on Time Series

Q1 A gardener records the temperature in her greenhouse every 2 hours over a 12-hour period. Her results are shown in the table below.

	0900	1100	1300	1500	1700	1900	2100
Temperature (°C)	27	28	30	31.5	30.5	29	28

a) Draw a time series graph to show this data.

b) Use your graph to predict the temperature at 16:30.

Q2 The table below shows the population of a village, recorded every six months for four years.

	2000	2001	2002	2003
Jan-Jun	770	710	650	620
Jul-Dec	750	670	660	580

a) Draw a time series graph to show this data and draw a trend line.

b) Use your trend line to predict the population in the period Jan-Jun 2004.

Edexcel Everyone
AQA Higher only

Q3 A shoe shop recorded the total number of pairs of shoes sold every 3 months from January 2001 to December 2003. The information is recorded in the table below.

	Jan-Mar	Apr-Jun	Jul-Sep	Oct-Dec
2001	2150	2270	1950	2480
2002	2850	2820	2780	3110
2003	3250	2950	3300	3440

a) Draw a time series graph to show this data and draw on a trend line. Use the trend line to predict the number of pairs of shoes sold between Jan and Mar 2004.

b) Calculate and plot a 4-point moving average for this data on the same graph.

c) Use these moving averages to draw a line of best fit and use this to predict the number of pairs of shoes sold in the period Jan-Mar 2004.

d) Which answer is the most reliable, a) or c)?

e) How many pairs of shoes do you think they will sell in total in 2004?

Questions on Time Series

Another Higher page — there's a lot of them in this section.

Higher **Q4** The takings in a bed and breakfast by the sea are largely dependent on the weather. The takings (in £) in 2001 to 2003 are shown in the table below.

	Jan-Mar	Apr-Jun	Jul-Sep	Oct-Dec
2001	2600	4200	10 500	5000
2002	3000	5500	16 000	4800
2003	3400	6100	20 000	5400

a) Plot the data on a time series graph.

b) Calculate and plot the appropriate moving point averages.

c) Draw a trend line for the moving averages.

d) What is the seasonal effect for Jan-Mar 2002?

e) What is the average seasonal effect for 2002?

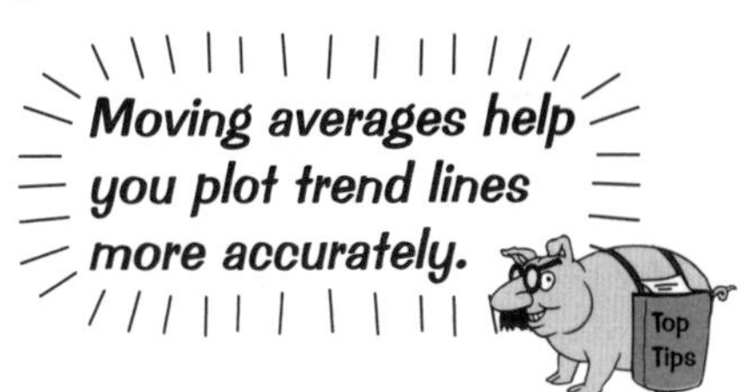

Higher **Q5** A tutor records his income from private tuition over each quarter. His results are shown in the table below.

	2001	2002	2003
Jan – Mar	2800	3010	3380
Apr – Jun	2230	2550	2820
Jul – Sep	1350	1620	1900
Oct – Dec	2560	2820	3280

a) Draw a time series graph to show this data.

b) Calculate and plot a 4-point moving average on the same graph.

c) Draw a trend line using your moving averages.

d) What is the seasonal effect for Jul-Sep 2002?

e) Calculate the average seasonal effect for Oct-Dec.

f) Use the trend line and the average seasonal effect to predict the tutor's private income for Oct-Dec 2004.

Questions on Quality Assurance

You don't need this page if you're doing Foundation.

Higher → **Q1** A manufacturer checks that the waist size of skirts being produced are the required 60 cm. A sample mean is taken every two hours and the results recorded below.

	0900	1100	1300	1500	1700
Mon	60	61	60	59	60
Tue	59	60	61	59	61
Wed	60	60	61	62	62

a) Plot each day's averages against the time.

b) Should any action be taken and if so, when and why?

Higher → **Q2** A coffee machine is checked every day for a week — the level of the liquid should reach 8 cm. A sample of the same number of cups is taken every morning and the median level recorded.

Day	Mon	Tue	Wed	Thu	Fri	Sat	Sun
Level (cm)	8.0	8.2	7.2	7.0	7.4	7.2	6.8

a) Plot these medians against the time.

b) Should the owner of the coffee machine have taken any action? Justify your answer.

Higher → **Q3** Boxes of tacks are advertised as containing about 40 tacks. The manufacturer makes regular checks to ensure the boxes contain the correct number. A sample mean is taken every two hours for three days and the results are tabulated below.

	1000	1200	1400	1600	1800
Wed	41	40	39	40	41
Thu	40	40	42	40	41
Fri	41	40	40	36	40

a) Plot each day's averages against the time.

b) Should the manufacturer be happy with the results? If not, why not?

Higher → **Q4** Three machines are used to make 55 cm long shoe laces. Samples are taken regularly from each machine and their mean length recorded below.

	1000	1100	1200	1300	1400	1500
Machine A	55	55	54	55	56	55
Machine B	55	54	55	56	53	58
Machine C	54	55	56	57	58	58

a) Plot each machine's sample means against the time.

b) Is machine A working properly? If not, why not?

c) Should any action be taken on machine B?

d) Is machine C okay? Give a reason for your answer.

If some of the averages are way out, then there are problems...

Questions on Correlation

Two variables can be positively correlated, negatively correlated or not correlated at all.

The first two questions refer to the following three graphs:

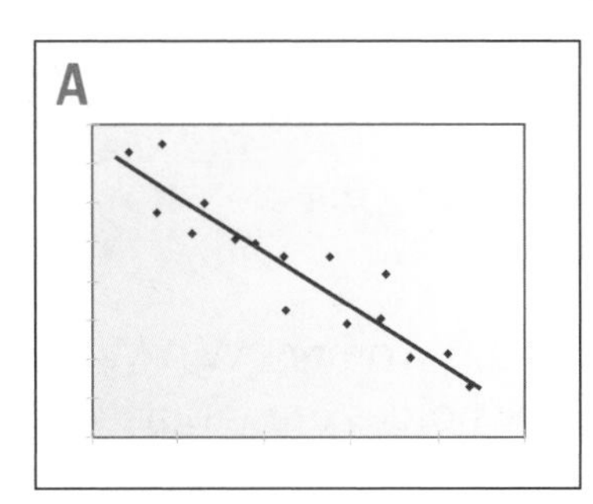

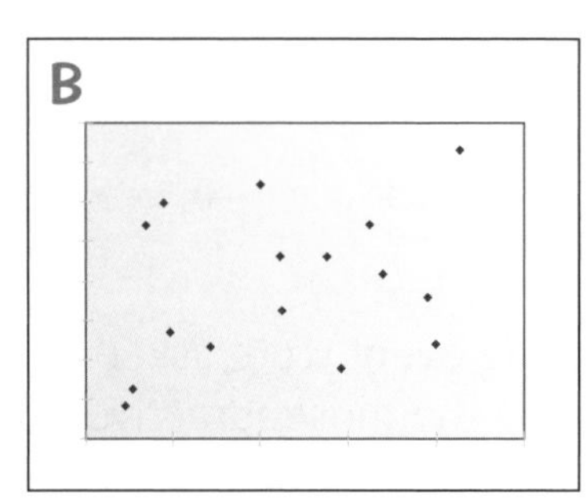

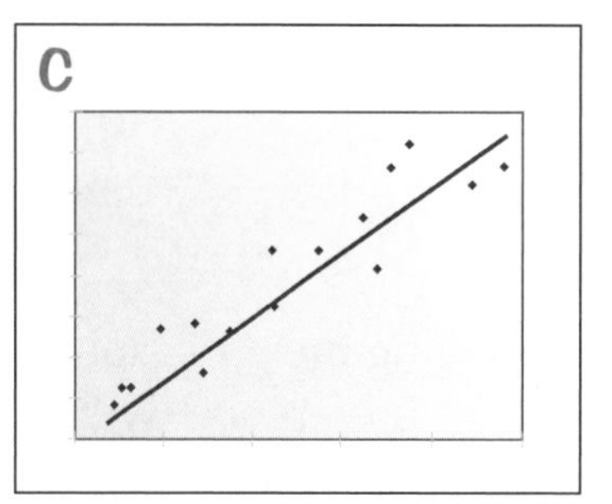

Q1 **a)** What is this type of graph called?

b) What type of correlation is shown in:

i) Graph A **ii)** Graph B **iii)** Graph C

Q2 For each pair of variables below, state which of the graphs is most like what you would expect if you plotted them against each other.

a) Outside temperature, number of visitors to the zoo

b) Age, number of pets

c) Number of hours spent on homework, number of hours spent watching television

d) Shoe size, life expectancy

e) Hours of sunshine, time spent in the garden

Causality means that a change in one variable causes a change in the other variable.

Q3 State which of the following pairs of variables, if any, have a **causal** link.

a) Height and weight

b) Speed of car, stopping distance

c) Temperature outside, heating bills

d) GCSE Mathematics score, GCSE History score

Q4 Using a suitable scale, plot variable A on the x-axis and variable B on the y-axis:

Variable A	190	100	220	290	260	30	150	270	30	140	70	240
Variable B	13	15	10	3	8	24	14	5	20	19	22	7

What type of correlation does the graph show?

Questions on Spearman's Rank Coefficient

***This page is Higher than a rather high thing** — but not as high as Snowdon.*

Higher **Q1** What range of values can Spearman's rank correlation coefficient take?

Higher **Q2** Which of the following correlation coefficients shows the least correlation?

0.9 **0.15** **–0.8** **–0.1** **0.95** **0.4**

Higher **Q3** Two young men at a speed dating event were asked to rank ten women, W1–W10, in order of preference (with 1 being the most attractive). Their choices are tabulated below:

	W1	W2	W3	W4	W5	W6	W7	W8	W9	W10
Romeo	5	6	3	2	9	1	8	10	7	4
Casanova	2	6	1	4	10	3	9	8	5	7

The Spearman's rank formula's given to you in the exam, so you can look it up if you need to.

a) Calculate Spearman's rank correlation coefficient for this data.

b) Do Romeo and Casanova have similar tastes in women?

Higher **Q4** Two friends at a wine tasting were asked to award marks out of ten for eight different wines, A–H. Their scores are shown in this table:

	A	B	C	D	E	F	G	H
Thelma	6	5	2	6	7	9	4	7
Louise	7	6	10	4	3	1	8	2

a) Copy and complete the table below to show how the two girls ranked each wine.

	A	B	C	D	E	F	G	H
Thelma					2.5	1		2.5
Louise			1					

b) Use these ranks to calculate Spearman's Rank Correlation Coefficient.

c) What does this tell you about their tastes in wine?

Higher **Q5** Judges Benchley and Court awarded marks to seven competitors, C1–C7, taking part in a gymnastics competition. These are shown in the table below:

	C1	C2	C3	C4	C5	C6	C7
Judge Benchley	8.7	9.4	8.0	9.2	7.6	9.0	8.7
Judge Court	8.9	9.5	8.2	9.0	7.7	9.1	8.7

a) Work out Spearman's rank correlation coefficient for this data.

b) How similar are the judges' rankings?

Questions on Working with Scatter Diagrams

The line of best fit should run close to as many of the points on the scatter diagram as possible. Ideally, it should go through the mean of both variables.

Q1 The table below shows the ages of a sample of boys and the number of packets of crisps they eat in an average week.

Age	10	7	12	16	13	12	15	11	8	15
Packets of crisps	3	10	1	5	12	7	8	4	2	3

a) Plot this data on a scatter diagram.

b) Is there any correlation? If so, draw a line of best fit.

Higher → **Q2** The diagram below shows the correlation between the results of two mathematics papers for a group of students.

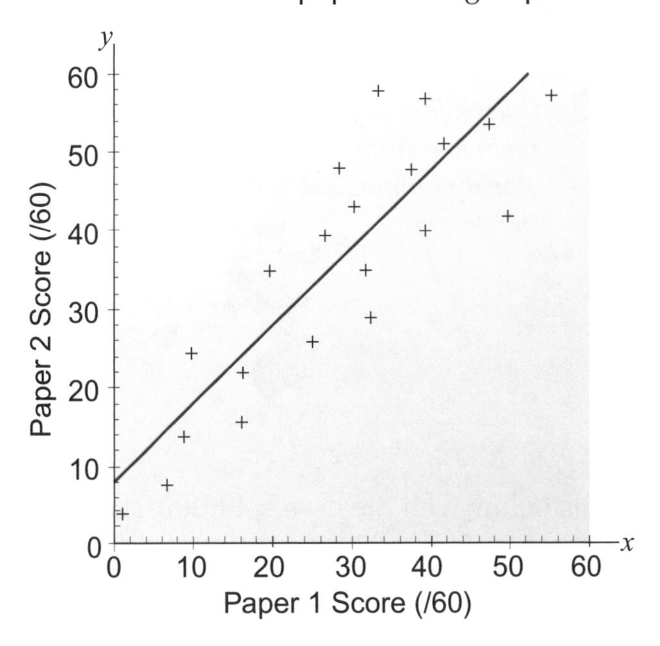

a) Work out the equation of the line of best fit shown.

b) What does the line of best fit tell you about the relative performance of the students in the two papers?

Q3 A van driver wanted to know if the load he carried affected the van's diesel consumption, so he recorded the details for several long trips he made:

Load (tonnes)	0.5	2.6	7.0	2.8	5.0	7.2	6.0	1.3	3.6	4.4
Miles per litre	6.9	6.3	4.3	5.9	5.2	4.6	5.0	6.7	5.9	5.6

a) Plot the data on a scatter diagram and draw a line of best fit.

b) Is there any correlation? What does this mean?

Higher

c) Work out the equation of this line.

d) What does the y-intercept tell you about the van's diesel consumption?

Questions on Working with Scatter Diagrams

The following questions refer to the scatter diagrams below:

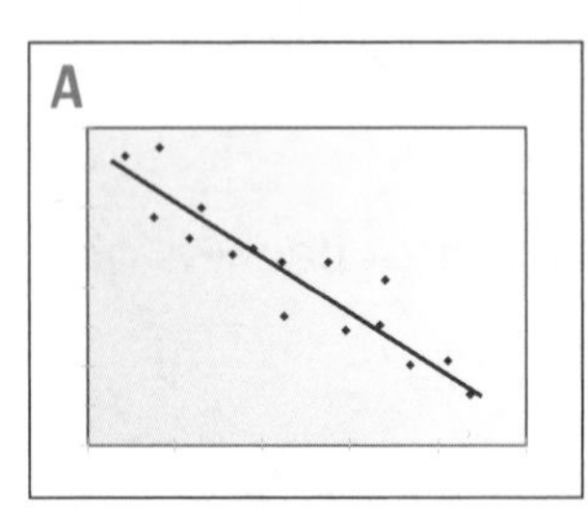

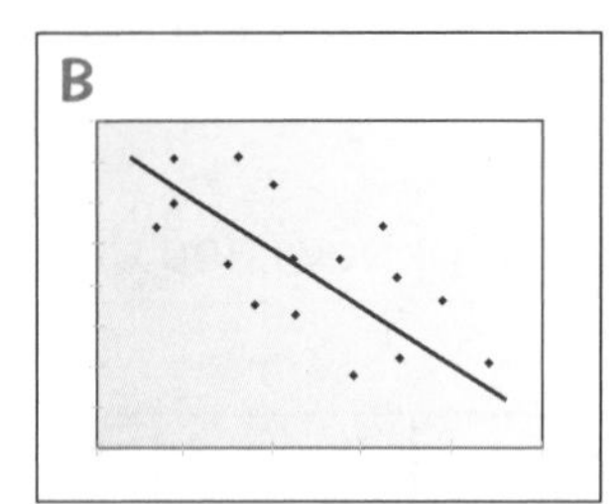

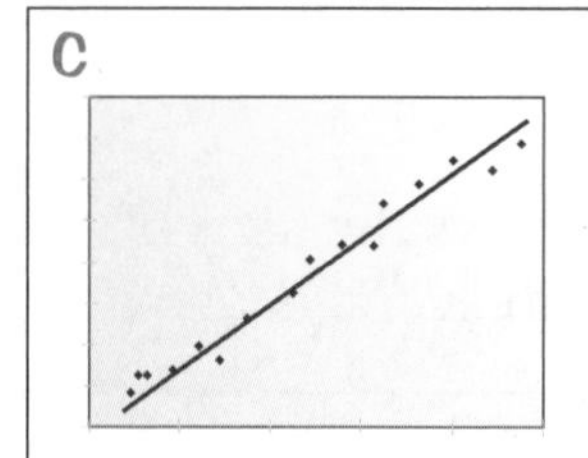

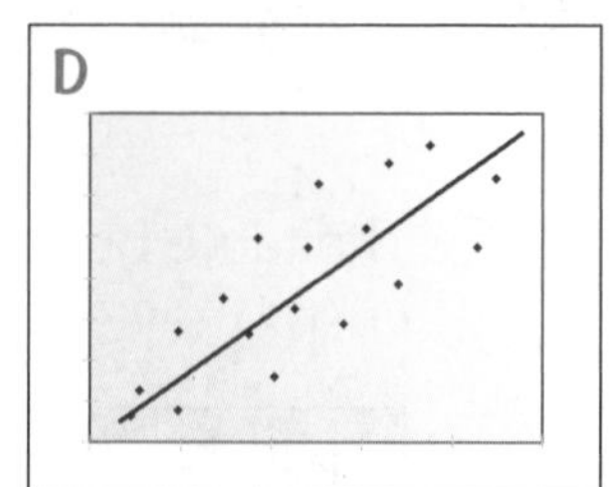

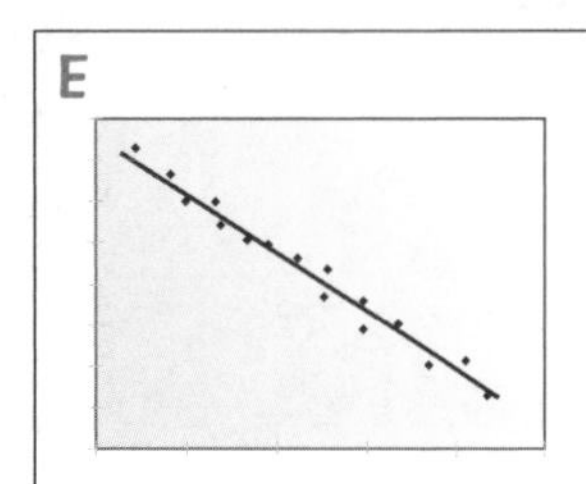

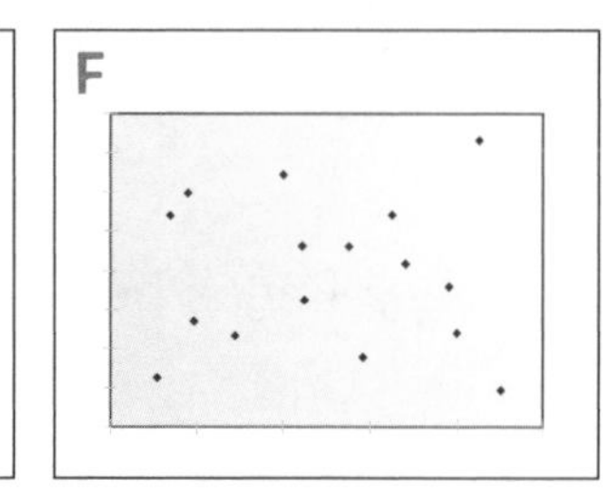

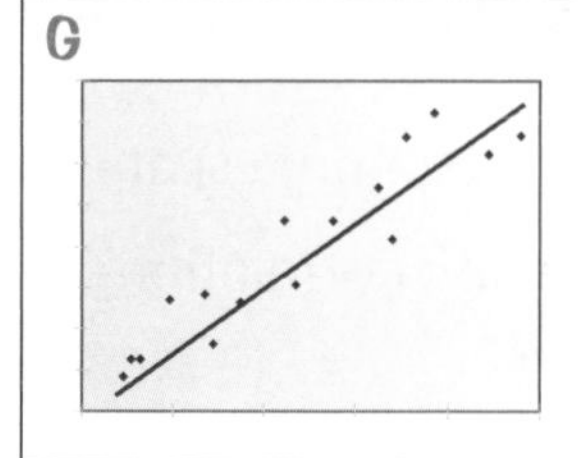

Q4 State which of the scatter diagrams above have:

a) strong positive correlation

b) no correlation

c) weak negative correlation

d) moderate positive correlation

e) moderate negative correlation

f) weak positive correlation

g) strong negative correlation

Q5 Match each of the correlation coefficients below with the corresponding scatter diagram.

a) –0.9

b) –0.75

c) 0.95

d) –0.4

e) –0.1

f) 0.45

g) 0.8

Q6 Below are four pairs of variables that relate to the scatter diagrams B, C, D and F. Which diagram is most likely to relate to each pair?

a) The force with which a ball is hit, the distance it travels

b) Time spent on computer, time spent watching television

c) Shoe size, money in bank account

d) Waist size, hat size

Questions on Interpolation & Extrapolation

This page is only for people taking AQA Higher.

Higher → **Q1** **a)** Define the term "interpolation".

b) Which is more likely to give you an accurate estimate — interpolation or extrapolation? Explain your answer.

Higher → **Q2** The number of tickets sold and the associated bar takings for some pub gigs are tabulated below:

Number of tickets sold	45	68	24	38	57	63	60
Bar takings (£)	340	560	150	290	510	600	550

a) Plot this data on a scatter diagram and draw a line of best fit.

b) If just 30 tickets are sold, how much money is the bar likely to take?

c) The maximum capacity allowed in the pub is 70. Estimate the bar takings then.

Higher → **Q3** Julia, a part-time waitress, was curious to know how much in tips she might earn if she turned full-time, and worked 38 hours a week.

She recorded the tips she received for various hours worked in the table below:

Hours worked	10	8	12	10	14	11	13	11	11
Tips (£)	40	33	42	38	48	41	39	38	40

a) Plot this data on a scatter diagram and draw a line of best fit.

b) Find the equation of the line of best fit.

c) Estimate, by using this equation or otherwise, how much in tips Julia could hope to receive working full-time.

d) How accurate would you expect her estimate to be? Explain your answer.

Extrapolation is when you predict a value outside the range of the data set.

Questions on Estimation of Population

A lot of populations are too big, or too hard to track down, to be able to do a census. You can use samples to estimate population statistics.

Q1 Hazel has a large number of slugs in her garden. To find out what type of slug they are, she needs to know their lengths. She measures ten slugs in total, with the following results:

12 cm	14 cm	12.5 cm	11.5 cm	13.5 cm
13 cm	12 cm	10 cm	11 cm	13 cm

a) Use Hazel's measurements to estimate the mean length of the slugs in her garden.

b) How or why might this result be inaccurate?

Q2 A farmer has 30 equally populated henhouses. He collected and counted the eggs from six of these houses on the same day, with the following results:

37	42	35	47	42	37

a) How many eggs, on average, does each of these henhouses yield?

b) How many eggs would the farmer expect to get altogether each day?

Q3 Name an accurate (and practical) way of estimating the size of a population of wild deer.

Q4 Some Durham University students conducted an opinion poll to find out if their fellow students approved of top-up fees. They asked 100 students from each of four year groups. The results are tabulated below.

	Yes	No	Don't know
1st Years	10	80	10
2nd Years	15	80	5
3rd Years	25	50	25
4th Years	30	20	50

a) Based on the data in the table, estimate what percentage of university students agree with the introduction of top-up fees.

b) What do the majority of students think?

c) How could this estimate have been improved?

A sample needs to be big enough to accurately represent the population.

Questions on Estimation of Population

Q5 A meadow is populated by rabbits.
To estimate the size of the population, 20 were caught, tagged and released.
The next day 24 were caught, and two were found to be tagged.

a) Estimate how many rabbits there were in the meadow.

b) Why did they need to be recaptured a day later rather than a week later?

Q6 Jean has 800 apple trees in her orchard. Fruit-pickers stripped ten trees, chosen randomly, and recorded the total weight of the apples taken from each tree:

52 kg	55 kg	49 kg	63 kg	60 kg
58 kg	48 kg	62 kg	55 kg	58 kg

Approximately what weight of apples can she expect to get in total from her orchard?

Q7 The first night's performance of a play was full to its capacity of 1000 and Sarah-Jayne had been asked to find out whether or not the audience liked it.

Which of the following would be a suitable sample size to form a realistic public opinion?

a) 5 **b)** 200 or **c)** 50

Q8 Eaton Forest is full of foxes and chickens. To try and find out how many of each were in the forest, 20 foxes and 50 chickens were caught, tagged and released. At the end of each of the next three weeks a number of each were caught, checked and released, with the following results:

	1st week		2nd week		3rd week	
	Caught	Found tagged	Caught	Found tagged	Caught	Found tagged
Foxes	24	4	22	3	18	2
Chickens	40	1	30	2	30	3

a) Based on the first recapture, how many foxes and chickens were there?

b) Assuming the number of tagged animals in the population remains constant over the three weeks of the study:
i) estimate how many foxes and chickens there were at the end of the 2nd week,
ii) estimate how many chickens there were by the end of the third week.

c) What do you think is happening?

The capture/recapture method allows you to estimate the size of a population of animals.

Questions on Probability

Remember: the probability of any event happening must lie between 0 and 1 — the more likely an event is to happen, the closer its probability will be to 1. If you get a bit confused, try drawing a scale like the one below.

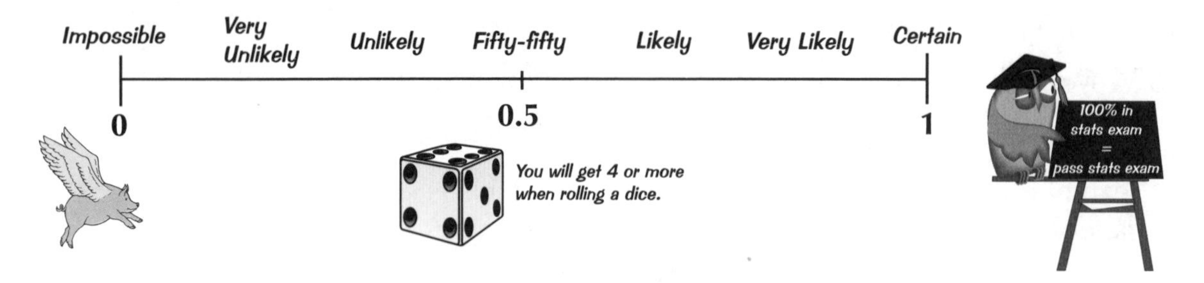

Q1 Draw a probability scale from 0 to 1, labelling the points 0, 0.1, 0.2, ..., 1.
Mark points a, b and c on your scale to show how likely you think each of these events is:

a) A van that is less than a year old will break down in the next year.

b) A van that is 50 years old will break down in the next year.

c) A van that is 10 years old will break down in the next year.

Q2 Christina says that she has a probability of 1.4 of passing her GCSE Statistics exam. Explain why this isn't possible.

Q3 Two goats, Glenda and Gertrude, have a sprint race. If both goats finish the race, there are three possible outcomes. What are they?

Q4 a) For each of these spinners, decide the following:

i) Which number is most likely to be spun.

ii) Which number is least likely to be spun.

1. 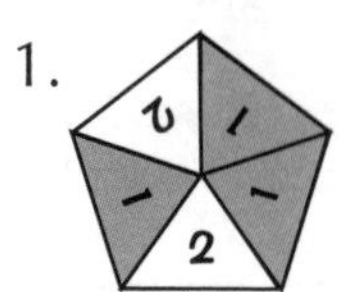 2. 3. 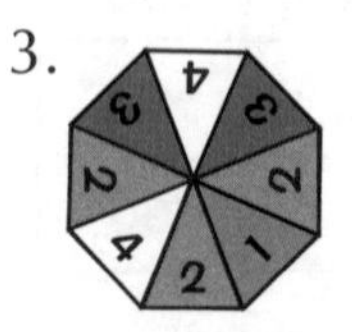 4. 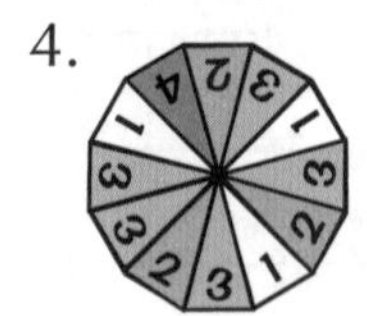

b) Draw a spinner with nine sections where each number is equally likely to be spun.

Q5 Louise and Gordon both want to go to Alton Towers. They can only afford one ticket. They decide to throw a standard dice to see who should go.

a) What are the possible outcomes they could get?

b) Gordon decides that if a 1, 2, 3 or 4 is thrown, he gets the ticket. Is this fair? Explain your answer.

c) Explain how they could use the dice to decide fairly.

Questions on Probability

These probability questions can be a tricky business. All you're really interested in is the number of ways an event can happen, compared to the total number of things that can happen. Remember that — and you're sorted.

Q6 David has 10 marbles in his pocket. He wants to show his friend his favourite marble. If he picks one marble at random from his pocket, what is the probability that it's his favourite?

Q7 Richard has been given a packet of mixed sweets. If he picks one sweet at random, he has a probability of 0.25 of picking a mint-flavoured sweet.

How many sweets are in the packet if there are seven mint-flavoured sweets?

Q8 **a)** Dorothy throws a standard dice. What is the probability that she will get:

i) an odd number?

ii) 2?

iii) an even number?

iv) a prime number?

Higher

b) What are the odds of Dorothy throwing a 3?

Don't forget — the 2 numbers in your odds ratio should add to give the total number of outcomes.

Q9 24 runners taking part in a marathon all have an equal probability of winning. Eight are women, and 16 are wearing tracksuits.

a) What is the probability of a man winning the race?

b) What is the probability of a person wearing a tracksuit winning the race?

Higher

c) What are the odds of a woman winning the race?

Q10 The results of a traffic survey are recorded below.

Type of vehicle	Red	Blue	Green	White
Car	12	12	5	3
Lorry	2	1	0	11
Motorbike	1	2	0	1

a) How many vehicles were counted in the survey?

b) A vehicle is selected at random from the survey. Find the probability that the vehicle is:

i) a red lorry

ii) a car

iii) a green motorbike

iv) blue

Higher

c) What are the odds that a vehicle selected at random from the survey will be a lorry?

Questions on Sample Space and Venn Diagrams

All these lovely diagrams — it's almost like art. And they're useful too. Diagrams make it much easier to work out probabilities as they show all the possible outcomes. So it might help to draw one even if you're not asked to.

Q1 Draw a sample space diagram to show all the possible outcomes of throwing a standard dice ***and*** spinning this spinner:

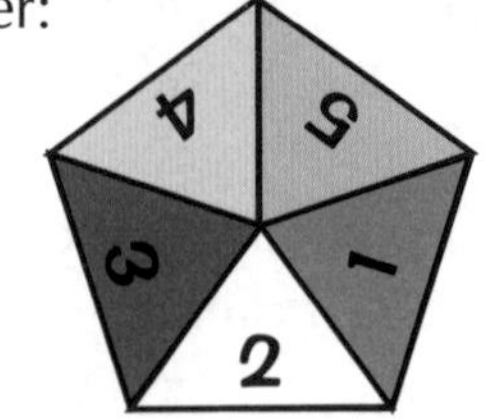

AQA Everyone
Edexcel Higher

Q2 Draw a Cartesian grid to show all the possible outcomes of selecting a suit from a pack of cards ***and*** picking a counter from a bag containing one green counter, one blue counter and one red counter.

AQA Everyone
Edexcel Higher

Q3 Roy has started to draw a Cartesian grid to work out the possible outcomes of throwing a standard green dice and a standard yellow dice.

a) Copy and complete the grid to show all possible outcomes.

b) Write down the probability of:

i) getting two odd numbers,

ii) getting a total of less than 8,

iii) getting two numbers whose difference is 3.

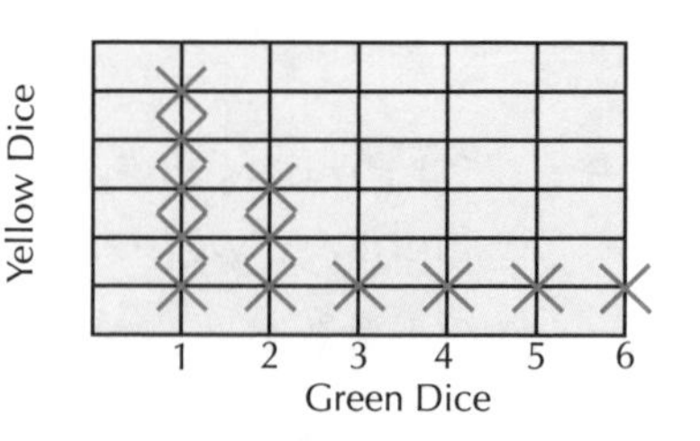

AQA Everyone
Edexcel Higher

Q4 A group of children on an outdoor pursuits course are given a choice of events to try. The results of who wants to do what are shown below:

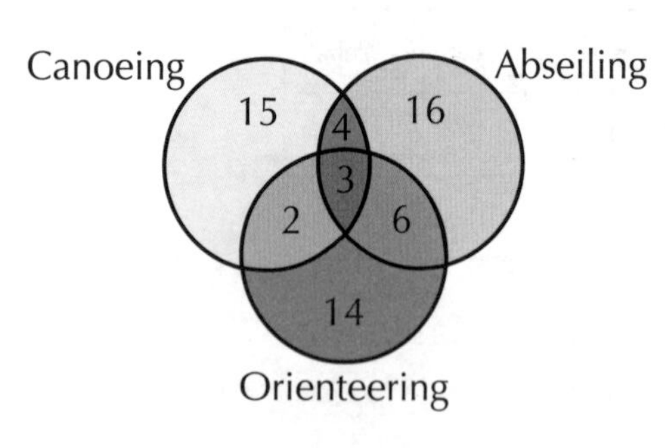

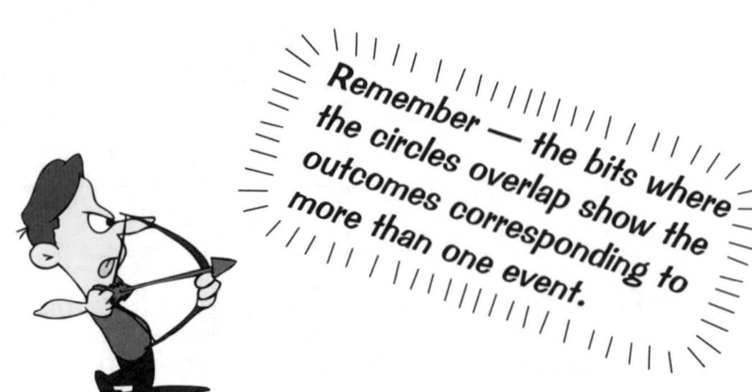

a) How many are in the group?

b) How many want to do canoeing?

c) If you picked a child from the group at random, what is the probability of him or her wanting to do all three activities?

d) What is the probability of the child only wanting to do orienteering?

Questions on Expected and Relative Frequencies

Relative frequency is for estimating probabilities and expected frequency is for predicting the frequency of an outcome when you already know its probability. Make sure you know which is which — and the formulas for each.

Q1 A standard dice is thrown 50 times. What is the expected frequency of:

a) numbers less than 4?

b) factors of 6?

c) a 5 being thrown?

Q2 A factory produces chocolate penguins which have a 5% probability of being misshapen, and boxes of chocolate frogs which have a 10% probability of failing a quality check.

a) The factory produces 280 chocolate penguins in an hour.
What is the expected number of misshapen penguins produced per hour?

b) 100 boxes of frogs are checked for quality each day.
How many boxes would you expect to pass the quality check each day?

Q3 Mike and his friends are brilliant at pub quizzes. For any quiz they enter, there are three possible outcomes — they win, finish second, or finish third or worse. The outcomes have probabilities 0.7, 0.2 and 0.1 respectively. This month they will enter 10 pub quizzes.

a) Copy and complete this table showing the expected frequencies of each outcome:

Outcome	First	Second	Third or worse
Expected Frequency	$10 \times 0.7 = 7$		

b) This table shows the results of the quizzes.

Quiz	1	2	3	4	5	6	7	8	9	10
Outcome	1st	1st	1st	2nd	1st	1st	1st	1st	1st	1st

Draw a graph comparing the expected frequencies with the actual frequencies.

Q4 A six-sided dice is thrown 100 times and 45 fours are recorded.

a) Calculate the relative frequency of fours.

b) Do you think the dice is biased? Explain your answer.

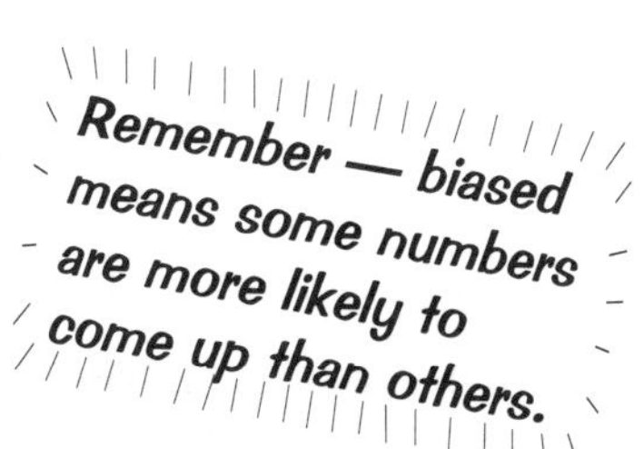

Q5 Dana and Sunil both support Foxfield Utd. The team are currently bottom of their league after winning only 5 out of 20 games this season.

a) Estimate the probability of the team winning a game.

b) There are 16 games left to play. Dana thinks they will win 3 of them, and Sunil thinks they will win 10. Who do you think is more likely to be right? Explain your answer.

Questions on Probability Laws

The first thing to think about when tackling one of these is to work out whether the events can happen at the same time — then you know which addition law to use. And remember: the probabilities of independent exhaustive events always add up to 1.

Q1 State whether the following pairs of events are mutually exclusive.

a) When picking a card at random from a standard pack of cards:
'getting a heart' and 'getting an ace'.

b) 'Winning the National Lotto' and 'not winning the National Lotto' with the same set of numbers in the same draw.

c) When selecting a person at random from a group of joggers:
'getting a man with black trainers' and 'getting a man with white shorts'.

d) When throwing a dice:
'getting a 6' and 'getting a 4'.

Q2 Daphne has a box of crisps that contains 3 packets of cheese and onion, 5 packets of roast chicken and 4 packets of salt and vinegar.

Daphne selects a packet from the box at random. Find the probability that she gets:

a) cheese and onion

b) roast chicken

c) cheese and onion or salt & vinegar

Q3 George uses the spinner below to decide which kind of film to see. Each section represents a different film, and they each fall into one of three mutually exclusive categories. 'A' means he'll see an action film, 'C' a comedy, and 'S' means science fiction.

Find the probability that the film he selects is:

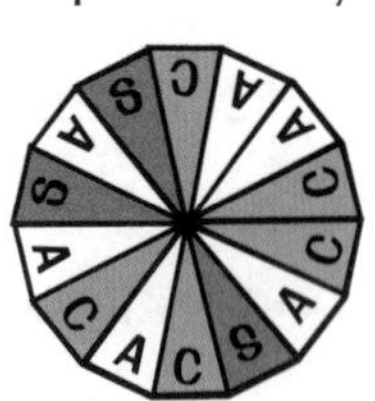

a) a comedy

b) action or a comedy

c) not action or comedy

Q4 Carolyn picks a card at random from a standard pack of 52 cards.

a) What is the probability of Carolyn getting a club or getting a heart or getting a spade?

b) What is the probability of Carolyn not getting a 5?

Higher

c) Calculate the probability of Carolyn picking a heart or a number less than 4.

d) Calculate the probability of Carolyn selecting a jack or a spade.

Q5 Alicia and Ben enter a raffle. There is a single prize which will be awarded to the person who owns the selected ticket. Of the 50 tickets available, Alicia buys 30 and Ben buys 20.

Calculate the probabilities of each winning the raffle.
Are these events exhaustive? Explain your answer.

Questions on Probability Laws

There's always one rule for one and one rule for another, isn't there? Events which have no effect on each other are independent. Otherwise they're dependent. Make sure you know the difference and the two multiplication laws.

Q6 Gillian is designing a new school sweatshirt. She selects a colour by putting the names of five colours (green, red, blue, burgundy and black) in a bag and randomly selecting one. She then tosses a coin to decide whether the sweatshirt should be round-necked or V-necked.

Calculate the probability of Gillian choosing:

a) a green round-necked sweatshirt

b) a black V-necked sweatshirt

c) a red sweatshirt with any neckline.

Q7 'Malcolm's Car Sales' have a new car to be won. All you need to do is throw a 6 seven times in a row with a standard dice.

a) Calculate the probability of winning the car.

Higher → **b)** What are the odds of winning?

Q8 The probabilities that Katie and Daniel will go to France this summer are 0.6 and 0.3 respectively. Assuming that these probabilities are independent, find the probability that:

a) they will both get to France

b) only one of them will get there

c) neither Katie nor Daniel will go to France this summer.

Higher → **Q9** A glass jar contains 25 pink balls, 5 white balls, 17 green balls and 13 blue balls. Two balls are picked at random and are not replaced.

a) i) Find the probability of the first ball being pink.

ii) Find the probability of a white ball followed by a green ball.

b) If three balls are taken from the jar and not replaced, calculate the probability that a blue ball is picked, followed by two white balls.

Higher → **Q10** A family decides to go for a picnic. There are a mixture of sandwiches: 6 ham, 8 cheese and 11 peanut butter. Each person randomly receives three sandwiches, starting with the daughter who only likes ham. What is the probability that she will get three sandwiches that she likes?

Questions on Tree Diagrams

Tree diagrams are really useful for working out probabilities. They're bound to come up in the exam, so make sure you can do them. Don't forget — you can easily check your diagrams by making sure that the end results add up to 1.

Q1 Gemma goes to watch a netball tournament after school. There are three matches. The probability of her watching any one match is 0.4.

a) Copy and complete this tree diagram:

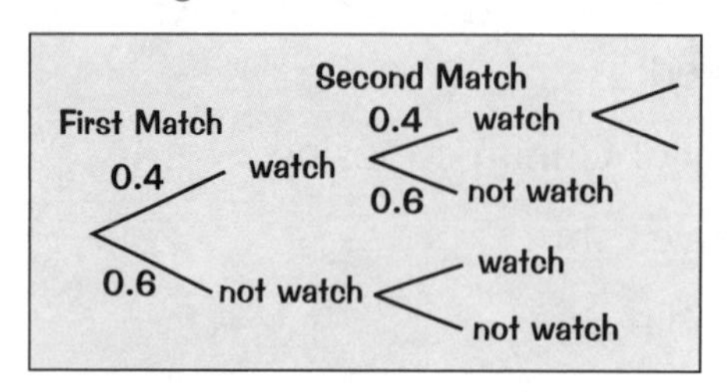

b) Find the probability of her watching the first two matches.

c) Find the probability of her watching any two matches.

d) Find the probability of her watching all three matches.

Q2 From the tree diagram below, calculate the probability of passing both History and French.

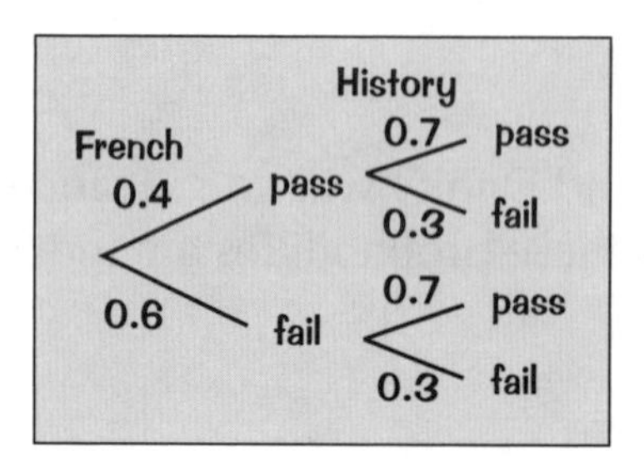

Higher → **Q3** There are two sets of traffic lights on the way into town. The probability that you have to stop at the first set is 0.6. The probability that you have to stop at the second set is 0.6 if you stopped at the first set, or 0.7 otherwise.

a) Draw a tree diagram to show the probabilities for both sets of lights.

b) Find the probability of getting through both sets of lights without stopping.

c) What's the probability that you will have to stop at least once?

Higher → **Q4** Matt and Simon play each other twice at tennis. The probability that Matt wins the first match is 0.7. If he wins the first match, the probability he wins the second is 0.5. If he loses the first match, the probability of him winning the second is 0.8.

a) Draw a tree diagram to show the probabilities for both matches.

b) Find the probability that Simon wins both matches.

c) What's the probability that they win one match each?

Questions on Discrete Probability Distributions

For all you Higher people, the table shows the start of Pascal's Triangle. Remember that each number inside the triangle is the sum of the two numbers above it.

Number of Trials	Coefficients in the expansion of $(p + q)^n$	Number of Different Combinations
1	1 1	2
2	1 2 1	3
3	1 3 3 1	4
4	1 4 6 4 1	5
5	1 5 10 10 5 1	6
6	1 6 15 20 15 6 1	7
7	1 7 21 35 35 21 7 1	8

Higher **Q1** The probability of a biased coin landing on heads is p, and the probability of it landing on tails is q. Using Pascal's triangle, find an expression for the probability that the coin lands on heads 3 times out of 5.

Higher **Q2** Marge is eating grapes from a very large sack (you can assume that each pick is independent of the previous one). Each time she chooses a grape from the bag, there is a 15% chance that it will be damaged.

a) What is the chance that she will find exactly one damaged grape amongst the first three she chooses?

b) Marge chooses 7 grapes from the sack. What is the probability that exactly two of them are damaged?

Higher **Q3** At a garden centre, you can buy mixed bags of bulbs containing daffodils and tulips. When the bags are packed, each bulb is chosen at random with the probability of choosing a daffodil being 0.75 and the probability of choosing a tulip being 0.25. Each choice is independent of the previous one.

a) Out of a bag containing four bulbs in total, find the probability of two of them being tulips.

b) If a gardener buys a bag with six bulbs altogether, what is the probability that he gets exactly twice as many daffodils as tulips?

c) If a bag contains seven bulbs, find the probability of it containing more tulips than daffodils.

Answers

Answers: P.1 – P.8

Section One — Data Collection

Data Sources P.1

1. a) Primary data.
   b) Primary data.
   c) Secondary data.
2. a) Using any data source that has been compiled and processed by someone else, such as data from books, databases, the internet, magazines or newspapers.
   b) E.g. it may not be relevant to what you are trying to find out, it may be inaccurate, or it may be biased.
3. a) Secondary data.
   b) Two disadvantages are:
      i) the data may be biased because Wonderme have a vested interest in promoting their cream,
      ii) the data is 4 years out of date.
4.

Data	Primary or Secondary
Data from the 2001 census on the number of rooms in a house.	Primary
Results from an experiment measuring sizes of spider webs.	Primary
A pie chart in a magazine showing preferred beauty products.	Secondary
A grouped frequency table compiled by a supermarket showing the number of times customers visit the supermarket each month	Secondary

5. a) Secondary data.
   b) The data is not relevant to Cuthbert's project. Only two of the sample are of school age.
6. a) Any sensible answer including:
      i) The data is produced by Phloggit Advertising and so may be biased.
      ii) The graph has no scales on the axes.
   b) Secondary data.

Types of Data P.2

1. a) Quantitative data is data that can be measured with numbers.
   b) Qualitative data
2. a) Qualitative
   b) Quantitative
   c) Quantitative
   d) Qualitative
3. a) Discrete
   b) Any discrete data set, e.g. number of pupils in a class
   c) Continuous data is data that can only be measured to a certain degree of accuracy.
   d) Any continuous data set, e.g. times, heights, weights, etc.
4. a) Any item of data that cannot be measured numerically, e.g. music types, types of format sold, names of customers, etc.
   b) Any item of data that can be measured numerically, e.g. takings for each day, prices of CDs, amounts spent by customers, etc.
5. a) Discrete
   b) Continuous
   c) Discrete
   d) Continuous
6.

Data	Discrete or Continuous
Tail-bone lengths of dinosaurs collected in archaeological sites in America	Continuous
Number of people passing through Heathrow airport each day.	Discrete
Number of red blood cells in a collection of 10 ml blood samples.	Discrete
Times taken to be served in a fast-food restaurant.	Continuous

Classifying Data P.3

1. a) Ben's classes are subjective – it depends on the taste of the person putting the clothes into the classes.
   b) The 5 classes should be well-defined and cover all possibilities, e.g. Tops, Trousers, Jackets, Shoes and Other.
2. a) A categorical scale of measurement is a scale of measurement using numbers which have no meaning other than as class labels.
   b) i) A categorical scale of measurement.
      ii) No — the numbers only represent ranks.
3. a) Interval scale
   b) Categorical scale
   c) Rank scale
   d) Ratio scale
4. a) Rank scale
   b) Categorical scale
   c) Ratio scale
5. a) An interval scale of measurement is one in which equal steps on the scale are equivalent, and there is no true zero.
   b) For example, any temperature scale or calendar system.

More on Types of Data P.4

1. a) 0, 6, 11 and 16
   b) 0-5, 6-10, 11-15 and 16-30
2. a)

Length of time (mins)	1-10	11-20	21-30	31-40	41-60
Frequency	5	10	5	5	5

   b) Detail is lost.
3. a) 10 students
   b) False – 2 students got less than 40%
   c) 588 words
4. a) 8 households
   b) 16 households
   c) 3 households
5. a) Discrete bivariate data
   b) Continuous bivariate data

Census Data P.5

1. A population is the group of things under consideration in any statistical investigation.
2. a) All 20- to 30-year-old women
   b) All the public parks in London
   c) All the squirrels in Britain
   d) All football players in the Premier League
3. A census is a survey or statistical project which collects data on every member of a population.
4. It would be difficult to carry out a census because the population is not well defined. It is impossible to tell the difference between male and female stripy swamp alligators before they reach the age of 2. It would also be hard to judge if some alligators are under 5 years old.
5. a) No
   b) Because they would have to wear out every tyre — and they'd have none left to sell.
6. a) All the residents of Lancashire
   b) It is hard to know exactly who lives in Lancashire because people often move around. It would also be very time-consuming and expensive.
7. a) All the supporters of Moreton United
   b) It is difficult for Moreton United to get a list of exactly who their supporters are.
8. a) All the moorland dung beetles in the UK
   b) Because it would be extremely difficult and impractical for him to be sure that he had investigated every single moorland dung beetle in the UK.

Sampling P.6–8

1. a) Carrying out a survey on a proportion of a population (rather than every member). The sample must be representative of the whole population.
   b) Possible answers include:
      i) It's often more practical to collect than census data.
      ii) It's cheaper to collect.
      iii) It's quicker to collect.
2. Reason 1 – The sample is too small
   Reason 2 – The average wage of three people who are the same age might be misleading — e.g. a 13-year-old will probably earn less than a 19-year-old.
3. The sample is biased because it doesn't include anybody under the age of 18, and 92% of the people interviewed were over 35. Also, younger people are more likely to go to nightclubs.
4. a) Only 40% of people have replied to the survey. It may be that the other 60% of people were so dissatisfied with their cars that they didn't want to fill the form in.
   b) 30%

Answers: P.8 – P.13

5. **a)** Census data gives information about every single member of a population — it is possible that a sample will not be representative of the population it is drawn from.
   b) People who are ex-directory or who don't own a telephone are not included in the sample. This makes the sample biased.
6. Possible answers are –
   i) The sample is biased because all the members are from the same family, so are likely to have access to the same IT at home.
   ii) The sample is very small.
   iii) Some of the sample may not attend Beth's school.
7. Their samples were chosen at random from the sample frame, so some random variation is likely to occur.
8. A sample frame is a list or map of every single member of the population you are sampling from.
9. **a)** All the supporters of Whitby F.C.
   b) All people on the electoral register of Whitby
   c) Any reasonable answer, including:
   i) Not everyone on the electoral register will support Whitby F.C.
   ii) Some supporters may not be on Whitby's electoral register (e.g. because they're too young or live elsewhere)
10. **a)** All the lakes and ponds in Nottingham
   b) Either a list of all the lakes and ponds in Nottingham or a map showing all lakes and ponds in Nottingham.
11. Number the names in the list from 1 to 4000. Use a random number generator on a computer or calculator or use random number tables to get 500 different random numbers between 1 and 4000. The sample will be the 500 names with those numbers.
12. **a)** The sample is not random and so might not be representative of all the cakes.
   b) Use a random number generator on a calculator to get 5 different numbers between 1 and 50. Number the cake weights from 1 to 50. Select the cake weights with the numbers you have generated.
13. The company has sampled from the wrong population, as some people in the Rochdale telephone book may not be customers of the company.

Systematic & Stratified Sampling P.9

1. Divide 20,000 by 500 to get 40. Select a number at random between 1 and 40 – it could be 32. The sample would be the 32nd person on the list, then every 40th person until you have 500 people.
2. Advantage: It is easier to select a large sample with systematic sampling.
   Disadvantage: Systematic sampling may not give a representative sample when the population is made up from different groups or if there are periodic trends in the data.
3. **a)** Rounding to the nearest person, the sample would include: 10 receptionists, 5 salon managers, 25 colour technicians and 60 stylists.
   b) A stratified sample is likely to be more representative of the different employment types within the company.
4. **a)** The sample is not random and so will be biased.
   b) Rounded to the nearest person there would be 10 Year 7 students in the sample.
   c) The proportion of Year 11 students is 199/1600, which is roughly 1/8. As we know there are 10 Year 11's in the sample, the group must be 80 pupils.
5. **a) i)** To the nearest person there should be 7 male waiting staff in the sample...
   ii) ...and 5 female bar staff.
   b) The proportion of male chefs is 398/2000 which is roughly 1/5. So the sample size must be around 100.

Data Logging P.10

1. **a)** 100/30 = 3.33
   so, n = 4 because he wants to log fewer than 30 (if n = 3 then he'd log 33, but with n = 4 he'd log 25)
   b) 1, 87, 47, 86, 37, 81, 93, 68, 47, 56, 96, 27, 12, 31, 68, 64, 55, 25, 36, 88, 7, 31, 9, 6, 23.
2. **a)** and **d)** No, because you only need to take a few samples, so it's easier to do it manually.
   b) and **c)** Yes, because a large number of measurements is required.
3. **a)** Far less data to deal with than if the data was logged more often, so the analysis will be easier.
   b) The information is incomplete — you have no record of the number of people at the tills during other times.
   c) There are 24 items of data. This suggests 23 ten-minute periods or 3 hrs 50 mins.
   d) 6 is the correct mean of the data. However this isn't necessarily the mean number of people at the tills as you don't know how many there were in between photos.
   e) You don't know that there weren't more shoppers at times when no photos were taken.

Cluster & Quota Sampling P.11

1. One way to do this would be to choose a random sample of, say, 10 phone books, and then choose 100 names at random from each book. The number of phone books and the number of names from each book must multiply together to give 1000.
2. **a)** Quota sampling.
   b) Convenience sampling.
   c) Cluster sampling.
3. **a)** They could place an interviewer in the park and ask them to interview the first 500 people that they come across.
   b) The sample is biased – wherever the interviewer stands will be closer to some rides than others, so it is more likely that the people selected will prefer those rides.
4. Cluster sampling
5. 0.7% of 1000 is 7

Strengths & Weaknesses of Sampling P.12

1. A systematic sample could miss out the faulty tubs.
2. **a)** Simple random sampling.
   b) Advantage – It will produce an unbiased sample.
   Disadvantage – The households in the sample could be very spread out geographically, so the survey might take a long time and cost a lot.
3. **a)** Cluster sampling.
   b) The sample might not be representative of the whole of England and Wales because it is non-random.
4. **a)** Convenience sampling.
   b) The sample could be biased towards people who eat a lot of fast food.
5. **a)** Method 1
   b) The sample is only taken from those parents who drop their children off at school.
   c) Stratified random sampling.
6. Any sensible answer, including:
   i) subgroups can be hard to define
   ii) it can be expensive because of the extra detail involved.
7. **a)** When no sample frame is available.
   b) Quota sampling is non-random, so can give a biased sample.

Biased Samples P.13

1. **a)** Reason 1 – They have only sampled from one sixth-form college, instead of all the sixth-forms in the UK.
   Reason 2 – They have sampled from the wrong population – not all students at the college will be doing chemistry.
   b) They should have sampled from all sixth-form chemistry students in the UK.

Answers: P.13 – P.18

2. a) This is a convenience sample and is not random.
   b) They should have sampled from all the residents of Devon.
3. a) The sample is biased because it is non-random (chosen from people shopping on the high street) and because the proportions of the different age groups in the sample are different to the proportions in the whole of Yeovil.
   b) The council should have sampled from all the residents of Yeovil.
4. a) Cluster sampling.
   b) It is non-random.
5. a) Fred's sample is non-random – the people in it are likely to be commuters and are also people that already use public transport.
   b) Fred should use a random sample – e.g. a random sample chosen from the whole population of his town.

Planning an Investigation P.14-15

1. Sales of Freezee ice cream were better after the campaign than before the campaign, adjusted for the time of year.
2. The deck of cards has been stacked by Eddie.
3. Poxfix cures chickenpox.
4. Hypothesis 1 – The more TV that students watch, the heavier they are. Hypothesis 2 – The more TV that students watch, the worse their exam grades are.
5. a) Pete could test this hypothesis by collecting data on how often people do at least 20 minutes of exercise each week and measuring their resting pulse rate.
   b) This may have happened because different types of exercise have different effects on pulse rate.
   c) Pete could carry out a more detailed investigation looking at how different types of exercise affect resting pulse rate.
6. a) Students who attend the classes perform better than if they had not attended the classes.
   b) It might be that the students didn't attend the classes because they were already very good at statistics.
   c) You could test the students before and after the classes and see if their performance improves.
7. They could use a questionnaire to find out the age and sex of each person in a random sample and whether they are a fan of the band.
8. a) Clothes cleaned with Raz washing powder are whiter than clothes cleaned with any other brand.
   b) Carry out an experiment to compare the results of cleaning with Raz to cleaning with all other brands.
9. a) Recycling levels are higher since the collection service was set up.
   b) Collect data on levels of recycling before and after the service was set up.
10. a) Schools where sweets and crisps are sold have a higher proportion of overweight students than schools where sweets and crisps are not sold.
   b) The data is biased because students at the sports academy may be more likely to exercise and be more health-conscious, which would reduce the effect of the sweets and crisps on their weight.
   c) The health authority should collect data from schools which sell sweets and crisps and schools which do not sell sweets and crisps, making sure that each sample contains a wide range of schools.
11. a) There is a higher rate of road traffic accidents between 8 a.m. and 9 a.m. than during any other hour in the day.
   b) A questionnaire could be sent to a random sample of people asking whether they had been involved in a road traffic accident, and if so what time of day it occurred at.
   c) The police could use their own data on road traffic accidents, or data from car insurance companies.

Questionnaires P.16

1. a) It is likely that prison inmates will not answer this question truthfully in a face-to-face interview.
   b) Any sensible answer, including:
      i) You are more likely to get responses to a face-to-face interview
      ii) In a face-to-face interview the interviewer can explain the questions.
2. They may find that not everyone responds to their survey.
3. This question is not relevant to what the council wants to find out.
4. a) A pilot study can be used to find out any problems that you have not noticed with questions.
   b) The answers to the question do not cover enough possibilities, as the majority of people in the sample have answered other.
   c) Either change the list of answers to include more possibilities, or leave a space for people to write their favourite drink.
5. a) The question is biased towards Milko chocolate.
   b) Ask an unbiased question such as, "What is your favourite type of chocolate?"
6. a) The question is ambiguous because the age classes overlap, e.g. someone who's 30 could go in either the 18-30 or 30-40 group.
   b) Change the answers to:
      "i) Under 18
      ii) 18 to 30
      iii) 31 to 40
      iv) 41 to 60
      v) over 60".

Problems with Question Types P.17

1. The first two questions will tend to lead people to say that they disagree with the bypass.
2. a) The question is subjective – "very often" can mean different things to different people.
   b) Any sensible answer, e.g. "How many times a week do you visit the school canteen?"
3. a) Open
   b) Closed
   c) Open
   d) Closed
4. a) How do you travel to school?
   b) How do you travel to school? Tick one of the boxes.
      Bus ☐ Car ☐ Bicycle ☐
      Walk ☐ Other ☐
5. a) The data could be biased because of the low response to the questionnaire.
   b) He could follow up the people who have not responded.
6. Any sensible answer, including
   i) Sampling from the wrong population.
   ii) Low response rate.
   iii) Answers not being recorded accurately.
   iv) Losing data.

Opinion Scales & Random Response P.18

1. Opinion scales give more detail than a simple yes/no answer.
2. a) "How satisfied are you with the choice of books in the library? Give an answer between 1 and 5 where 1 means very unsatisfied and 5 means very satisfied."
   b) "Rate the standard of the food in the canteen. Give an answer between 1 and 5 where 1 means very poor and 5 means very good."
3. a) The question does not allow for much detail in opinions.

Answers: P.18 – P.22

b) "Do you agree that the new landfill site should be created?
1 Strongly disagree
2 Disagree
3 Neutral
4 Agree
5 Strongly agree"

4. Questions that people are likely to answer untruthfully.

5. The leader should write two questions. One should be the question of interest – e.g. "Do you smoke cigarettes?" and the other should be a dummy question e.g. – "Are you male?" Each member should answer one of the questions chosen at random without the leader knowing which question has been chosen. The youth group leader can then use what he knows about the number of males in the group and the fact that roughly half of the group will have chosen the dummy question to estimate the proportion who smoke.

6. You expect about 500 students to have answered yes because their coin showed heads. So 500 of the yes answers can be ignored. This leaves 632 – 500 = 132 out of 500 people who have answered yes to the question of interest.
$(132 \div 500) \times 100 = 26.4\%$
So an estimate of the proportion of students who eat one or more bars of chocolate every day is 26.4%.

Interviews P.19

1. Mr. Flyalot could be biased because of his wife's business.

2. a) More suited for interview because it's an open question.
b) Could be used in a questionnaire as it's a closed question.
c) Interview
d) Interview
e) Could be used in a questionnaire as it's a closed question.

3. Because people who have knowingly broken the law are likely to lie about it to an interviewer.

4. a) This is an open question, so a trained interviewer could ensure the answer was recorded correctly.
b) Make the question closed by using tick boxes, e.g.
"Which food do you most enjoy when eating out?
Italian ☐ Chinese ☐
Indian ☐ Other ☐".

5. a) Any sensible answers, including:
i) Postal questionnaires are cheaper than interviews.
ii) People are less likely to lie in a postal questionnaire.
iii) It's easier to post questionnaires to spread-out areas than to use interviewers.
iv) You don't have to worry about interviewers recording the data in a biased way.
b) Any sensible answers, including:
i) An interviewer can explain questions.
ii) You are likely to get a higher response rate.
iii) It's not likely that the wrong person completes the interview – this can easily happen with questionnaires.
iv) You can ask open questions which will give more detailed answers.
v) Answers to questions can be followed up by the interviewer.

Obtaining Data P.20–21

1. a) and b)
Any sensible answers, including:
i) *Hypothesis*: As fitness improves, the journey time should decrease.
Variables to keep constant:
Heart Rate, Route, Bike
Response Variable:
Journey Time.
ii) *Hypothesis*: As fitness improves, the average heart rate for each journey should decrease.
Variables to keep constant:
Journey Time, Route, Bike
Response Variable:
Average Heart Rate.
c) Any sensible answers, including:
i) Route. The route should be the same so she rides the same distance and includes the same hills, etc.
ii) Equipment. She should use the same bicycle.
iii) Weather. This could be kept constant by using an indoor track.
d) Any sensible answers, including:
i) Mechanical efficiency. An unavoidable puncture, etc. will affect journey time.
ii) Environmental: e.g. weather, road works, etc., will affect journey time.
iii) Illness. This might affect both heart rate and journey time.

2. a) (i) 3 min (ii) 5 min.
b) temperature is an independent variable; time is dependent.
c) Any sensible answers, including:
i) The type of photographic film
ii) The type of chemical solution
iii) The concentration of the chemical solution

3. a) There are enough tablets for 52 people $(730 \div 14)$. But, since there are a total of 100 people in the test, it would be sensible to give the tablets to half of the group (i.e. 50 people).
b) The remainder should form a control group.
c) When the experimental group receive their tablets, the control group should also be given a dummy tablet (placebo).
d) Any sensible answers, including:
i) Number of tablets taken
ii) Time of day that the pills are taken
iii) Diet of volunteers

4. a) i) Explanatory variable = model of ink cartridge
ii) Response variable = the number of pages printed before the cartridge runs out.
b) A fair test would keep all variables constant except those being tested. Any sensible answers, including:
i) use the same quantity of ink in every cartridge
ii) print the same page
iii) print on the same type of paper
iv) print using the same printer

5. a) A fair experiment would test a random sample of students both before and after their summer holidays. To keep it fair the following variables would need to be constant:
i) the same students should be tested in both tests
ii) the difficulty of the test paper should be the same
iii) the test should be sat by all students independently of each other
iv) the tests should be sat at the same time of day
v) any other sensible answer
b) The explanatory variable for this test would be the date (i.e. is it before or after the summer holiday?).
c) The response variable is the test score.
d) You could take the mean score from tests before the summer holiday and compare it with the mean score from tests afterwards.
e) The mean score before the summer holiday is 67.7 and after the holiday is 58.6. You could conclude from these results that students do forget subject knowledge over the summer holidays. But, to say this with any confidence you'd need a larger sample size (e.g. 100 students).

Surveys & Capture / Recapture P.22

1. a) You must assume that:
i) the samples have been selected randomly
ii) the samples are representative of the whole population
iii) the population size remains constant
iv) the original sample has had a chance to mix back into the whole population
b) $12/30 = 112/N$
So $N = 280$ fish
c) Any sensible answers, including:
i) it's only an estimate
ii) the second netting takes place soon after the original capture, so the tagged fish may not have mixed fully with the others in the water.

2. a) Rats: $70/N = 2/50$
So, $N = 1750$

Answers: P.22 – P.29

b) Mice: 30/N = 3/50
So, N = 500

c) Any sensible answers, including:
i) make sure that the samples are randomly taken and are representative of the population
ii) give the samples chance to fully mix back in with the population

3. a) Capture/recapture would only work well for populations (ii) and (iii).

b) Population (i) is not contained within the field, so it won't be constant.
Population (iv) can't move, so the tagged sample will never be able to mix back in with the rest of the population.
Population (v) grows too fast to measure in this way.

Simulation P.23

1. a) The table should be filled in with random 3-digit numbers from your calculator.

b) Any sensible method, including:
i) You could call '1' heads and '2' tails. Reading across the table, and ignoring other digits, it would start T,T.

ii) Do the same but only looking at the first digit of each 3-digit random number.
iii) Use all the digits in the table, read from left to right. This time let odd digits be heads, and even digits be tails. This is efficient as it includes all digits available.

2. a) 0

b)

1st Dice	4	4	3	3	3	3	2	6	5	1
2nd Dice	3	1	2	1	4	4	4	5	4	3
TOTAL	7	5	5	4	7	7	6	11	9	4

c) Her conclusion is incorrect as there are also six 4's. A much more reliable result could be obtained by using a larger sample size, e.g. 100

d) 7 is the most common theoretical total, but there aren't enough 'rolls' to draw a confident conclusion from this test.

Section Two — Tabulation and Representation

Frequency Tables P.24

1. a)

Pool Balls	0	1	2	3	4	5	6	7
Tally	卌 I	IIII	III	III	I	I	I	II
Frequency	6	4	3	3	1	1	1	2

b) 21

c) No. The table doesn't tell you how many times she won, because even if none of her balls were left, you can't tell if she potted the black before her opponent.

2. a) 14

b) 8

c)

Number of birds	0	1	2	3	4	5	6	7	8	9
Tally			I	II	IIII	II	II	II	I	
Frequency	0	0	1	2	4	2	2	2	1	0

d) 4

Grouped Frequency Tables P.25

1. a)

Score (s)	Tally	Frequency
3.0<s≤3.5	I	1
3.5<s≤4.0		0
4.0<s≤4.5	I	1
4.5<s≤5.0	I	1
5.0<s≤5.5	II	2
5.5<s≤6.0	III	3
6.0<s≤6.5	II	2
6.5<s≤7.0	III	3
s>7.0	II	2

b)

Score (s)	Tally	Frequency
3.0<s ≤4.0	I	1
4.0<s ≤5.0	II	2
5.0<s ≤6.0	卌	5
s>6.0	卌 II	7

c) There are far fewer classes. The table is therefore easier to read.

d) The class width s > 6.0 contains three of the original groupings, whereas the other new classes contain only two of the previous groupings each (especially important as scores are more concentrated in higher groups).

2. The class widths are not well defined. For example, it is not clear if the year 1980 is included in the first or second class.

Simplifying and Analysing Data P.26–28

1. a)

Distance (m)	0<m≤10	10<m≤20	20<m≤30	30<m≤40	40<m≤50	50<m≤60
Frequency	3	12	11	4	1	1

b) Rounding might have resulted in some of the distances being put in the wrong class. For example, a distance of 10.4 m is greater than 10 m, but after rounding it would be put in the 0<m≤10 class.

c)

Distance (m)	0<m≤20	20<m≤40	40<m≤60
Frequency	15	15	2

d) The first and second groups now have the same frequencies. This masks the fact that most of the distances were between 10 and 30 metres.

2. a)

Year	2000	2001	2002	2003
Total	167	184	203	217

b) The total number of animals sold increased each year.

c) All the detail about the sales of individual animals has been lost. The original table shows that the only animals which have increased their sales each year are the rabbits. These large increases have caused the increase in totals. However, the number of stick insects sold has actually fallen each year.

3. a) 63%

b) 30%

c) 'Used to Smoke' is the most stable across the four years.

d) i) The proportion of teenagers who 'regularly smoke' increases dramatically over the four years,
ii) while the proportion of those who have 'never smoked' decreases significantly during the same period.

4. a) 45% (43-47 acceptable)

b) 28% (26-30 acceptable)

c) Other answers were given that have not been included in the diagram.

d) The diagram shows a decrease in the % of people feeling that crime increased. This does not mean that fewer people thought this. There may not have been the same number of people in the sample each year.

5. a) The proportion is decreasing for both genders.

b) About 6% more women smoked.

c) The difference in genders appears to be closing. In 1992 it was zero.

d) About 20-25% if the trends continued.

e) The male rate drops from 110 to about 60 (per 100,000). This is roughly a 50% change.
The female rate increases from 20 to 30 (per 100,000). This is an increase of 50% .
So, the journalist is correct.
(But this report might be a bit misleading because it doesn't say that the male rate is still much higher than the female rate.)

Bar and Pie Charts P.29

1. a) About 75%

b) About 61%

c) Any sensible answer, including:
i) The number of people in each gender group may be different, yet the numbers of married men and women could be the same.
ii) Jenny might be assuming that men and women marry within the same age range.

d) On average, women live longer than men, and the husbands are usually older. So, women in their 90s are far more likely to have lost their husbands than men in their 90s are to have lost their wives.

Answers: P.29 – P.32

2. i) First work out the angle per pupil:

Year Group	Pupils	Angle / pupil
10	30	360°÷ 30 = 12° per pupil
11	20	360°÷ 20 = 18° per pupil

ii) Then work out the angles:

Will watch the match?	Year 10 frequencies	Angle to represent response
Definitely	6	6 × 12° = 72°
Very Likely	4	4 × 12° = 48°
Likely	2	2 × 12° = 24°
Unlikely	8	8 × 12° = 96°
No Way	10	10 × 12° = 120°

Will watch the match?	Year 11 frequencies	Angle to represent response
Definitely	4	4 × 18° = 72°
Very Likely	10	10 × 18° = 180°
Likely	6	6 × 18° = 108°
Unlikely	0	0°
No Way	0	0°

iii) Now draw a pie chart for Year 11 with these angles (and a radius of 3 cm — see below).

iv) Work out the area:
$\pi r^2 = 3.14 \times 3^2 = 28.26$ cm².
So the area per person in this pie chart is 28.26 cm² ÷ 20 people = 1.413 cm² per person.

v) Use this to work out the area then the radius of the Year 10 pie chart:
Area: 1.413 cm² per person × 30 pupils = 42.39 cm²
$\pi r^2 = 42.39$ cm²
So $r = \sqrt{(42.39/3.14)} = 3.7$ cm.

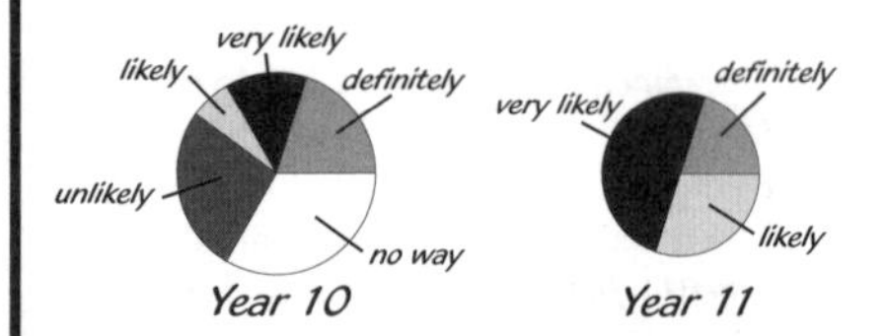

Discrete Data & Frequency Polygons P.30

1. a) 8

b)

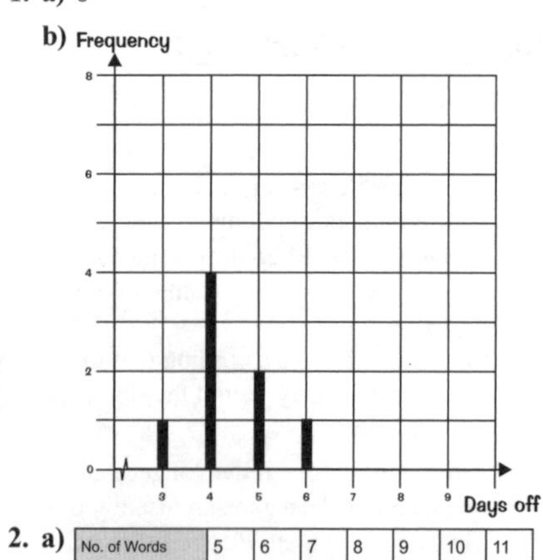

2. a)

No. of Words	5	6	7	8	9	10	11
Tally	||	~~||||~~	~~||||~~ |	|||	||	|	|
Frequency	2	5	6	3	2	1	1
Cum Frequency	2	7	13	16	18	19	20

b)

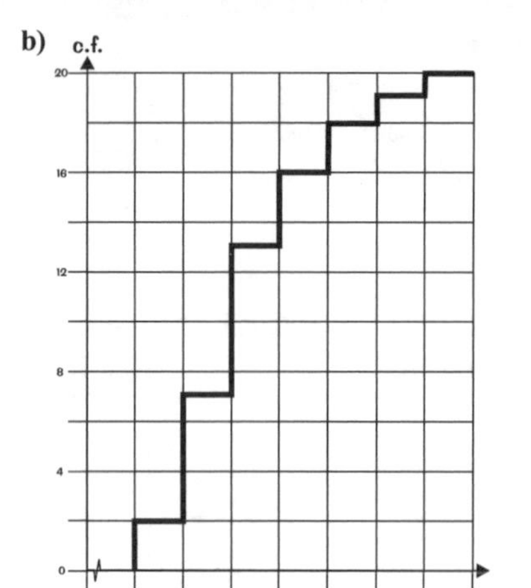

c) 7

Other Diagram Types P.31–32

1. a) 14

b) 12

c)

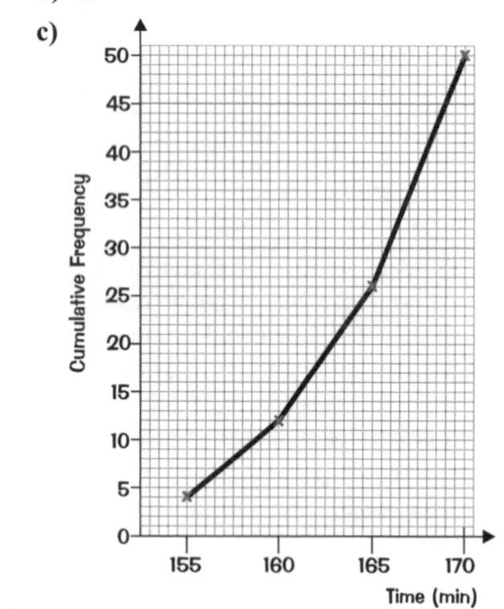

2. a)

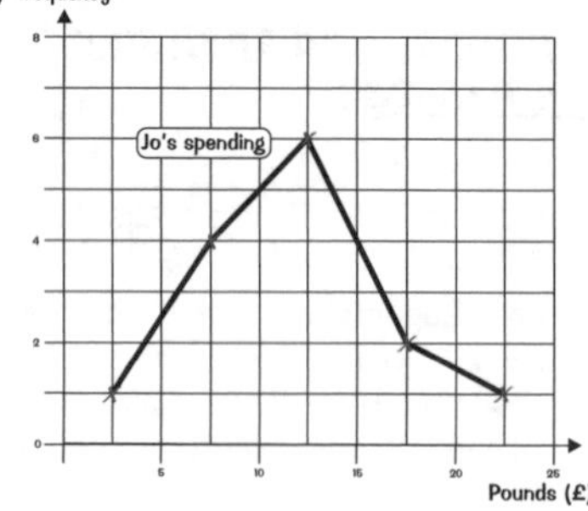

b)

c) IQR = 18.5 – 12.5 = £6 (ish)

d)

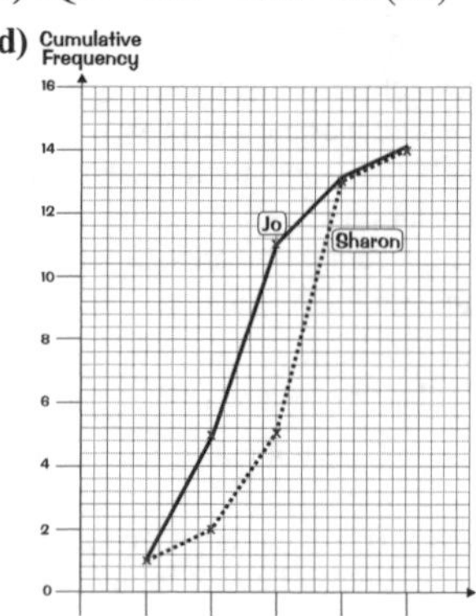

e) Jo: £11 or £12, Sharon: £16 or £17. Sharon seems to spend more. Her polygon is more to the right of the graph.

f) Because the data is grouped, it is not possible to tell if on any of the nights Jo might have spent £14.99 while Sharon spent £15.01 (i.e. very nearly the same amount). The grouping has lost the detail you would need to decide.

3. a) Brazil: 6.8+6.3+6.0+6.8+6.1+5.9 = 37.9% (±0.5%)

France: 2.4+2.4+2.8+2.2+2.2+2.7 = 14.7% (±0.5%)

b) Brazil has a much higher proportion of young. So the birth rate is probably higher, and the death rate is probably higher too.

c) i) male: 1.6+1.2+0.7+0.4 = 3.9 % (±0.5%)

ii) female: 2.7+2.3+1.5+0.8 = 7.3% (±0.5%)

d) Females tend to live longer in France.

e) The birth rate has fallen over the last 20 years.

4. a) 0800 – 0900: f.d. = 100 cars ÷ 1 hr = 100 cars per hr
0900 – 1200: f.d. = 90 cars ÷ 3 hrs = 30 cars per hr
1200 – 1400: f.d. = 80 cars ÷ 2 hrs = 40 cars per hr
1400 – 1530: f.d. = 75 cars ÷ 1.5 hrs = 50 cars per hr

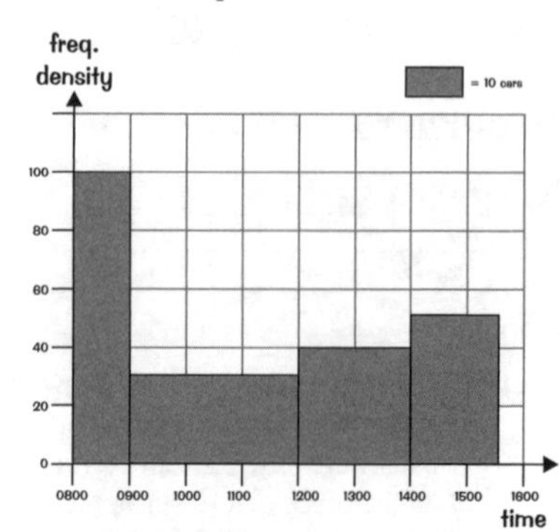

b) The frequency density of 150 represents 75 cars in half an hour.
75/30 = 2.5 cars per minute.

Answers: P.33 – P.39

Stem & Leaf Diagrams and Shading Maps P.33

1. a) 8 – 10%

b) £20,136 – £25,150

c) Wales

d) High income and low unemployment.

e) North-east England

f) There are errors in both keys:
Map 1's class widths are badly defined e.g. an unemployment rate of 10% could be placed in two classes.
Map 2's key contains classes that do not meet e.g. an average income of £20,110 would not fit into any of the classes.

2. a)

7	0
6	1, 6
5	0, 2, 2, 9
4	3, 4, 5, 5, 5, 8
3	1, 2, 7

KEY: 7 | 0 = 70 seconds

b) Mode = 45 seconds

c) Range = 39 seconds

Transforming Data P.34

1. a)

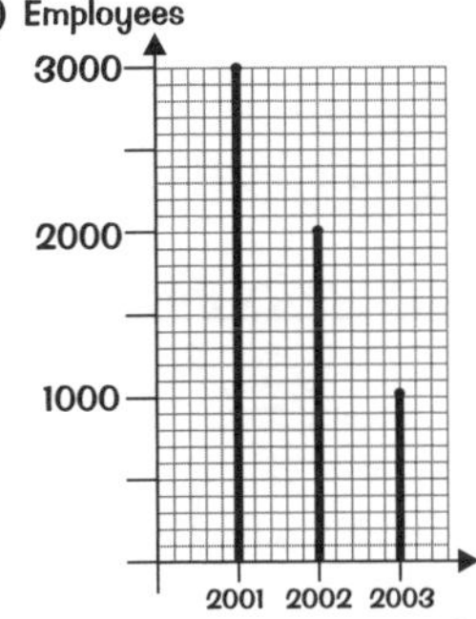

b) There is a constant rate of decline.

2. Total sweets = 6 + 18 + 12 = 36
So 1 sweet = 10°
Red = 6 ×10° = 60°
Blue = 18 × 10° = 180°
Green = 12 × 10° = 120°

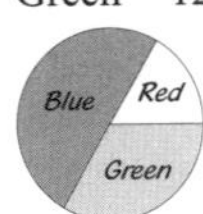

Frequency Distributions P.35

1. a) Spinners A&B:
i) Symmetric distribution
ii) Range = 9 – 5 = 4
iii) Mode = 7
iv) Median = 7

b) Spinners C&D:
i) Positive skew
ii) Range = 9 – 5 = 4
iii) Mode = 5
iv) Median = 6

c) Spinners E&F:
i) Negative skew
ii) Range = 8 – 5 = 3
iii) Mode = 7 and 8
iv) Median = 7

2. a) Totals are:
A: 1000, B: 1950, C: 1500

b) Proportions are:
A: 600/1000 = 3/5
B: 650/1950 = 1/3
C: 500/1500 = 1/3
So, village A has the highest proportion of people in their 60s. (*which is pretty obvious from the diagram.*)

c) Village A: Symmetric
Village B: Positive skew
Village C: Negative skew

Scatter Diagrams & Line Graphs P.36

1. parts **a)** and **b)** are shown on the graph.

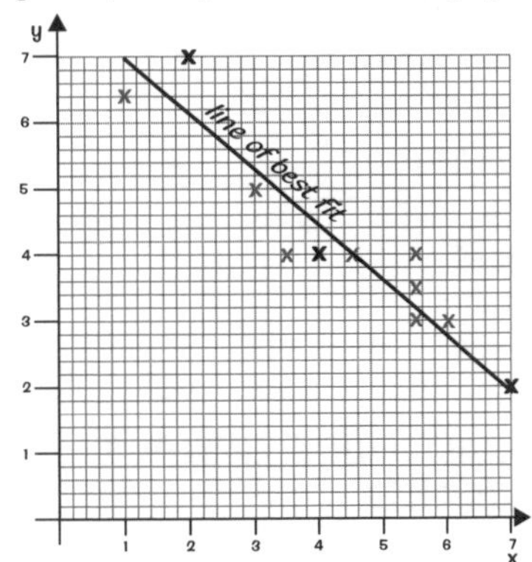

c) As x increases, y decreases.
There is a negative correlation between x and y.

d) Between 5.0 and 6.5 (depending on the line of best fit drawn).

2. a)

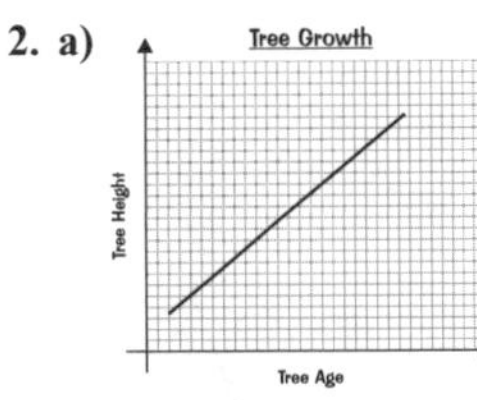

b)

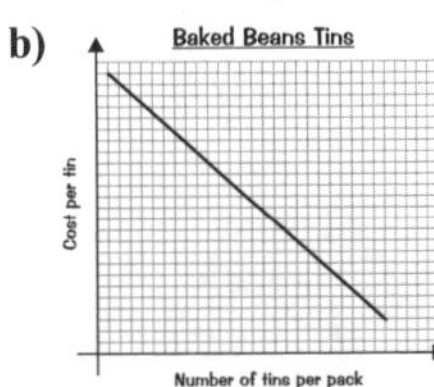

c)

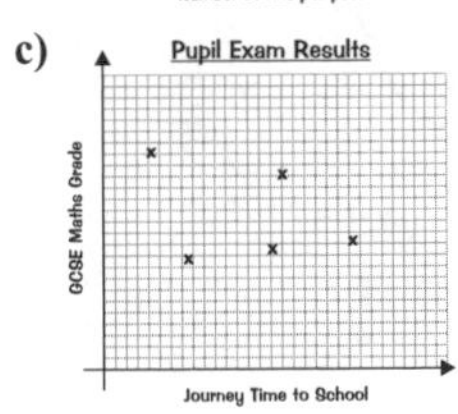

More Diagram Types P.37

1. a) Correct: Pair 1, Pair 2, Pair 5
Misleading: Pair 3, Pair 4

b) PAIR 3: The 2nd practice diagram has an area four times that of the first. This is not representative of the target being hit twice as often.
PAIR 4: The 2nd diagram has a volume 8 times as large as the 1st. Again this is misleading.

2. Area of Kayleigh's circle: $\pi \times 3^2 = 9\pi$
So, the area of Amy's circle is:
$9\pi \times 3 = 27\pi$.
Radius (R) of Amy's circle:
$\pi R^2 = 27\pi$
$R = \sqrt{27} = 5.196$ cm
So, the diameter = 10.4 cm

Problems with Diagrams P.38

1. a) The 1994 Africa height is over half the 2025 height, but the width of the diagram has increased as well — so the area of the 2025 diagram is about double the area of the 1994 one, and is therefore correct.

b) Any sensible answer, including:
The figures overlap, which is a bit misleading because you cannot see the entire area of each figure.

2. a) You can't really agree or disagree unless you look at the original data. Given the temperatures for the other months, it seems very unlikely that the temperature for April would be 0 °C, but you would need to check the original data before being certain.

b) The uneven scaling makes it look as if the temperature rise from May to June and from June to July is greater than from July to August, when in fact it's the same.

Spotting Errors in Diagrams P.39

1. a) Pictogram

b) 2.5 CO_2 symbols.

c) The pictograms are only correct if you round the data to the nearest 50 million BTU/person/year (it looks like the US and Canada use 7 times as much energy per person as Asia, but it's actually over 10 times as much).

d) According to the data the US&C should have two and a half people symbols, and the Asia pictogram 51, not 25

2. a) Any 3 errors, including:
i) 7.30 is either plotted wrongly or mislabelled.
ii) There is no title.
iii) Both x- and y-axis should be truncated.
iv) The y-axis is not labelled.

Answers: P.39 – P.47

b) Your solution must have at least three improvements from (a).

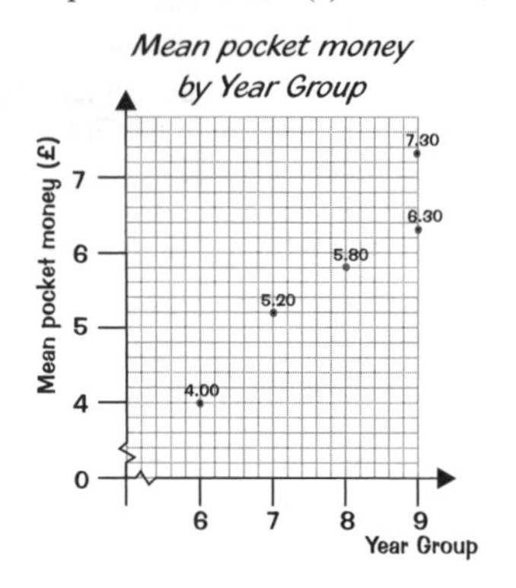

(*N.B. You should show both Yr 9 points in your solution.*)

Section Three — Data Analysis

Mean, Median and Mode P.40–42

1. **a)** 32.82/20 = 1.64 m (2 d.p.)
   b) 1.65 m
   c) 1.65 m
2. 108 – 75 = 33 years old
3. **a)** 2 hrs 40 mins.
   b) 2 hrs 38.5 mins
4. 5 and 6
5. 55%
6. **a)** 685/120 = 5.71 (2 d.p.)
   b) 6
   c) 5
7. **a)** 10847.5/95 = 114.2 (1 d.p.)
   b) You don't know the original data values any more, so you just have to use the midpoint value of each group.
   c) 111-130
   d) 91-110
8. **a)** Mean. The winner must have scored more points overall than the loser.
   b) Eric. His mean score of 66.15 is bigger than Nick's, which was only 60.5.
9. **a)** 4150/40 = 103.75 kg
   b) 90-110 kg
   c) 90-110 kg
10. **a)** The median. With such a small sample and a rogue value (90), the mean would be distorted.
   b) The mode. There are no two values the same – and even if there had been it could just be a lucky coincidence.
   c) He should use a much larger sample.
11. It can be used with qualitative data.
12. **a)** Mean.
   b) Mode. This is qualitative data, so it is uncountable.
   c) Median. Most tennis points are won from the serve or from a series of rallies. Points won from the serve will distort the mean and probably confirm the mode as 1. The median is likely to be the most useful.
   d) Mean. This is the most accurate. The median would be okay if the sample was very large.
13. 6.7%
14. Fixed rate of 7.5%. The other rates combine to give 7.49%.

Range and Quartiles P.43

1. **a)** 1020 – 80 = 940
   b) 510
   c) 700
   d) 840
2. **a)** 65 g
   b) The 5th decile (or D_5)
   c) 72 g
3. **a)** 325
   b) 340
   c) 303
   d) The 99th percentile
4. **a)** 38
   b) 29
   c) 29

Interquartile & Interpercentile Range P.44

1. **a)** 26 – 16 = 10 cm (allow 9 – 10 cm)
   b) 14.5 (allow 14.5 – 15 cm)
   c) 31 – 11 = 20 cm (allow 19 – 21 cm)
2. **a)** 200
   b) 240 – 160 = 80
3. **a)**

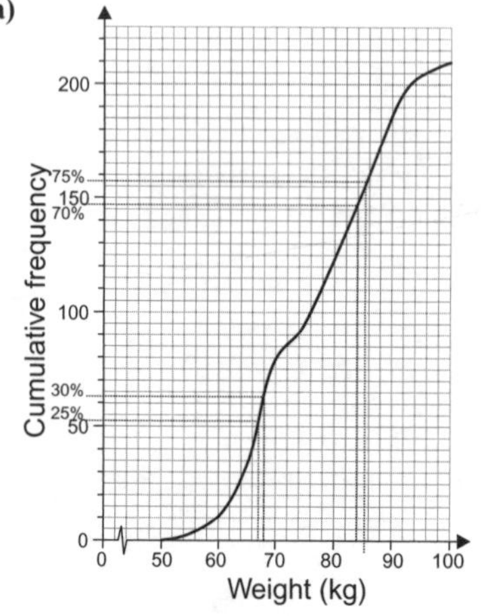

b) i) 85 – 67 = 18 kg
ii) 69 kg
iii) 83 – 69 = 14 kg

Variance & Standard Deviation P.45

1. 1.02
2. **a)** Mean = 68.5
   b)

x	x-x̄	(x-x̄)²
64	–4.5	20.25
71	2.5	6.25
68	–0.5	0.25
79	10.5	110.25
62	–6.5	42.25
73	4.5	20.25
67	–1.5	2.25
64	–4.5	20.25

   c) Standard Deviation = $\sqrt{\sum(x-\bar{x})^2/n}$ = 5.27
3. 2.87
4. Standard Deviation = $\sqrt{\sum x^2/n-\bar{x}^2}$ = 4.15
5. **a)** 85.89 kg
   b) Variance = 0.0129 kg
   Standard deviation = 0.11 kg (2 d.p.)

Box & Whisker Plots P.46

1.

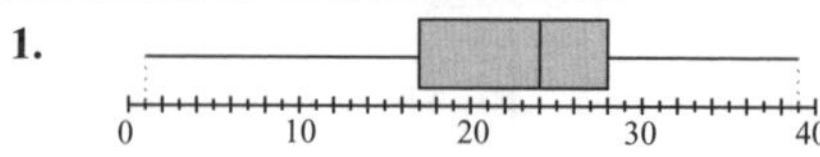

2. **a)** 25
   b) 57 – 7 = 50
   c)

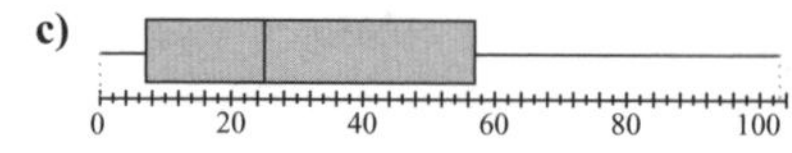

3.

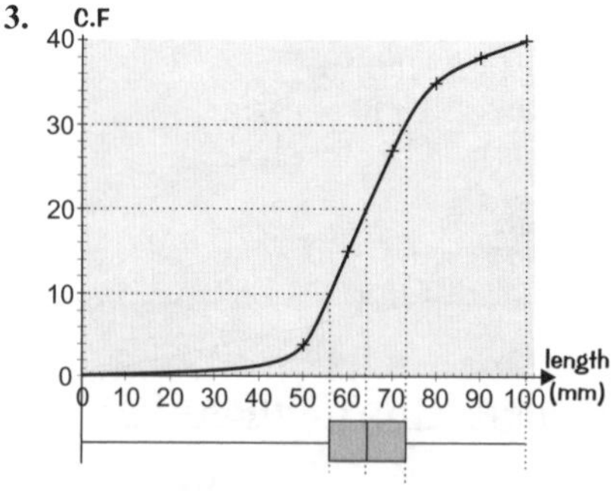

4. **a)**

0 20 40 60 80

   b) 79 and 88.
   c)

0 20 40 60 80

Standardised Scores P.47

1. **a)** (61 – 47)/8 = 1.75
   b) (52 – 58)/6.1 = –0.98 (2 d.p.)
   c) Geography, in which her standardised score is 3.27 (2 d.p.)

Answers: P.47 – P.54

d) –0.08 (2 d.p.)

e) Music, in which his standardised score is –2.95 (2 d.p.)

2. Ivy, with a standardised score of 0.662 (3 d.p.)

3. a) 47. Her standardised score was 1/6.

b) Laura. She had a standardised score of 4/9, whilst Jane's standardised score was 5/18.

Comparing Data Sets P.48

1. a) C. 50% of the marks were never more than one out and he or she was never more than two out on any one script.

b) A. More than a quarter of the marks were at least two out and the marks were four out on at least two occasions.

c) He or she is on average giving the script one less mark than specified so, if a mark is in doubt, he or she should award it.

2. a) B. The standard deviation was less than A's.

b) A. The range is greater than B's.

c) B. The mean is greater than A's.

3. a) C. The curve is lower, which means that there is a greater proportion of older people.

b) No. The cumulative frequency polygons only show percentages — he would need to know the total populations as well.

Summary Statistics P.49–51

1. a) 2000

b) 2003

c) (112/100) × 26 000 = £29 120.

d) (114/112) × 29 400 = £29 925

2. 120, 128.

3. a) The missing price is £815.10.
The missing index numbers are 110 and 104 (from right to left).

b) 108.68

4. a) 10

b) i) (66/58) × 100 × 15 = 1706.90 (2 d.p.)

ii) (155/144) × 100 × 10 = 1076.39 (2 d.p.)

iii) (145/130) × 100 × 6 = 669.23 (2 d.p.)

c) (1706.90 + 1076.39 + 669.23)/31 = 111.4

d) The average price of the ingredients to make their Yorkshire pudding has increased by 11.14%.

5. (432/28600) × 1000 = 15.1 (1 d.p.)

6. (15000/1000) × 21.4 = 321

7. a) 76.7 (1 d.p.)

b) The crude birth rate for women only would be much higher (about double). However the standardised birth rate for Hadham wouldn't change, irrespective of how the data was presented.
(NB this data may be affected by the fact that the average father is likely to be older than the average mother.)

c) The weights would stay in the same proportion, so the result would be the same.

8. Standardised male claim rate = 28.03
Standardised female claim rate = 25.82.
Since the standardised female claim rate is lower than that for men, women should get a better deal.

9. The number of firemen they insure from each age group, the number of claims that they have received from firemen from each age group and the standard population.

Time Series P.52-53

1. a)

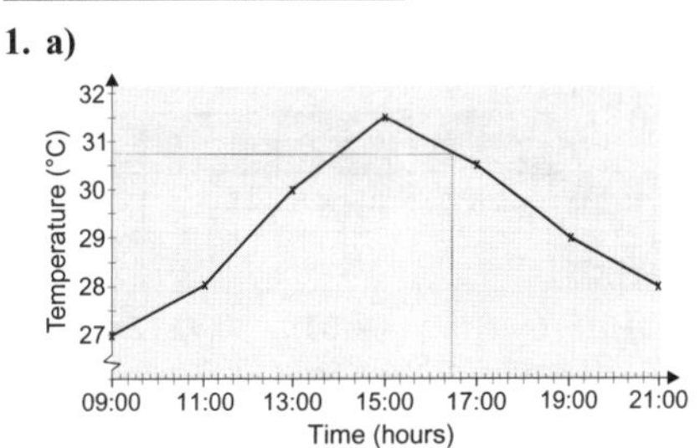

b) 30.75 °C (allow 30.5 – 31.0 °C)

2. a)

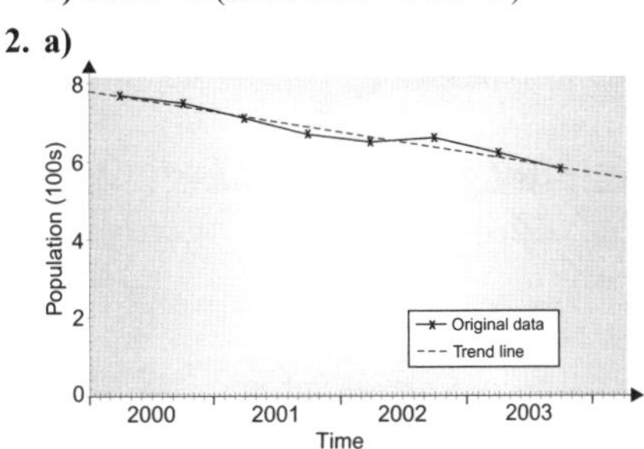

b) 560 (accept answer consistent with graph)

3. a)

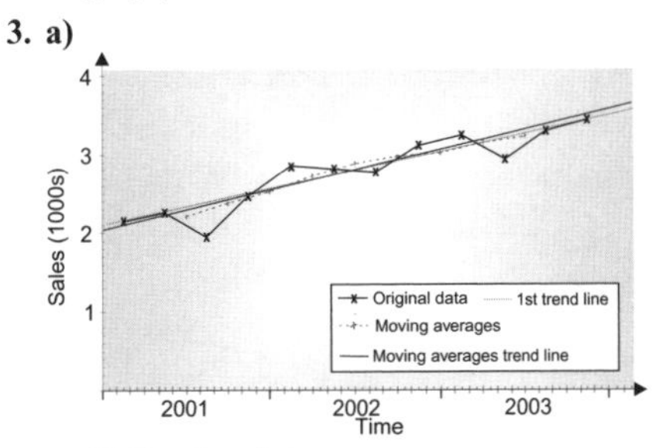

3560 pairs of shoes

b) Moving averages are 2212.5, 2387.5, 2525, 2732.5, 2890, 2990, 3022.5, 3152.5 and 3235.

c) 3620

d) The line drawn from the moving averages is the most accurate so c) is the most reliable result.

e) 3620 + 3750 + 3880 + 4000 = 15 250
(or take midway point and multiply by 4: 3810 × 4 = 15 240)

4. a)

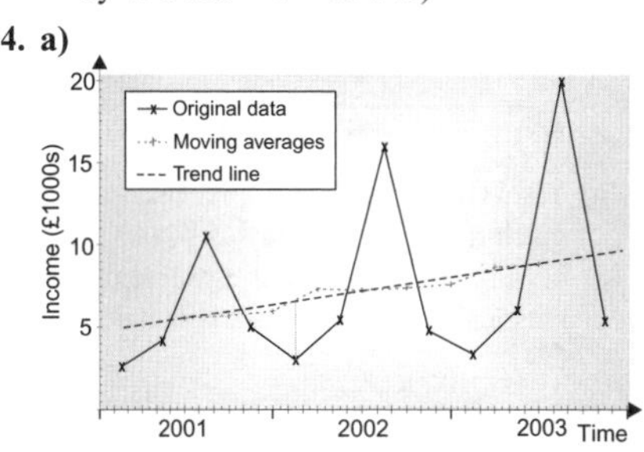

b) Should be a 4-point moving average.
Moving averages are 5575, 5675, 6000, 7375, 7325, 7425, 7575, 8575 and 8725.

c) See graph

d) 3000 – 6400 = –£3400

e) [–3400 + (5500 – 6950) + (16000 –7500) + (4800 – 8000)]/4 = £112.50

5. a)

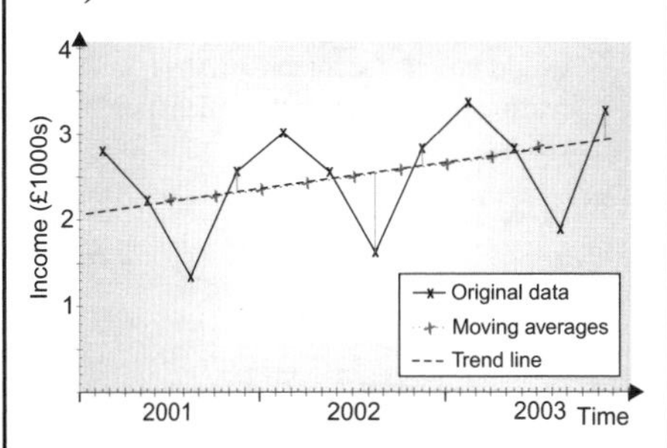

b) Moving averages are 2235, 2287.5, 2367.5, 2435, 2500, 2592.5, 2660, 2730, 2845.

c) see graph

d) Using trend line shown, seasonal effect = 1620 – 2550 = –£930
(accept answer consistent with graph and between –£950 and –£900)

e) [(2560 – 2330) + (2820 – 2630) + (3280 – 2930]/3 = £257
(accept answer consistent with graph)

f) 3230 + 257 = £3487
(accept answer consistent with graph)

Quality Assurance P.54

1. a)

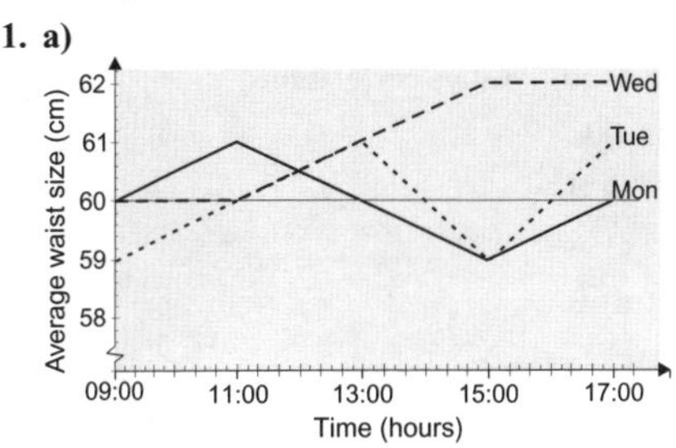

b) Yes. On Wednesday, when the samples taken were always on or above the target level. (Any reasonable answer with explanation is OK.)

Answers: P.54 – P.59

2. a)

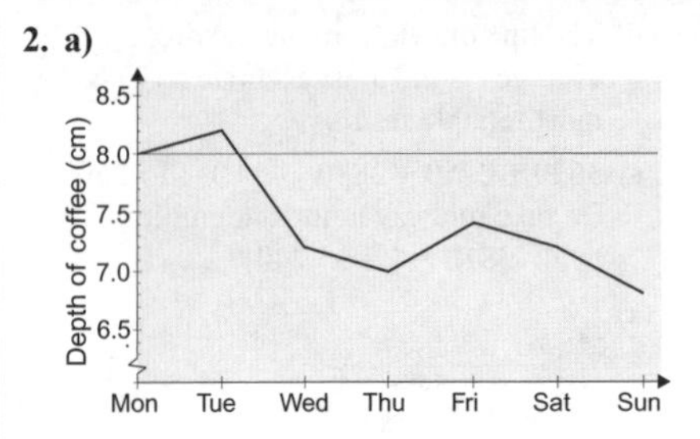

b) Yes. The owner should have serviced the machine on Wednesday as soon as it became clear there was a problem. (Any reasonable answer with explanation is OK.)

3. a)

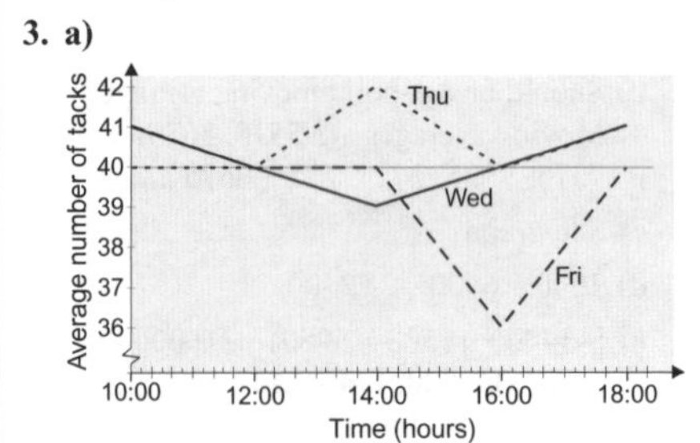

b) No. On Friday a mean sample of 36 would not be acceptable. (Any reasonable answer with explanation is OK.)

4. a)

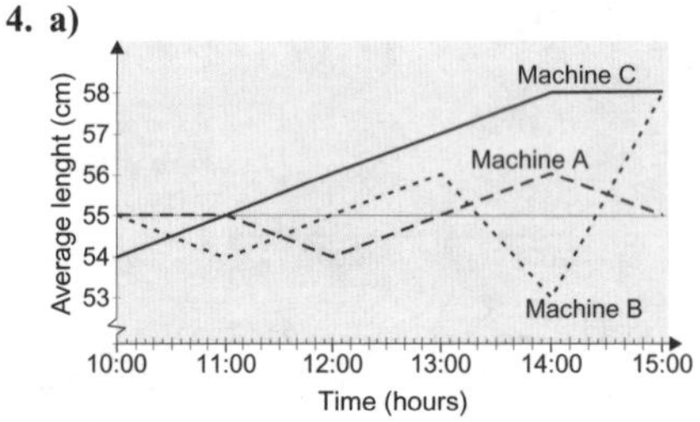

b) Yes.

c) Yes. The machine is becoming very inconsistent — the lengths of the laces are becoming more variable with time. (Any reasonable answer with explanation is OK.)

d) No. The lengths of the laces are increasing. (Any reasonable answer with explanation is OK.)

Correlation P.55

1. a) A scatter diagram

b) i) Negative correlation

ii) No correlation

iii) Positive correlation

2. a) C

b) B

c) A

d) B

e) C

3. b) and c)

4. a)

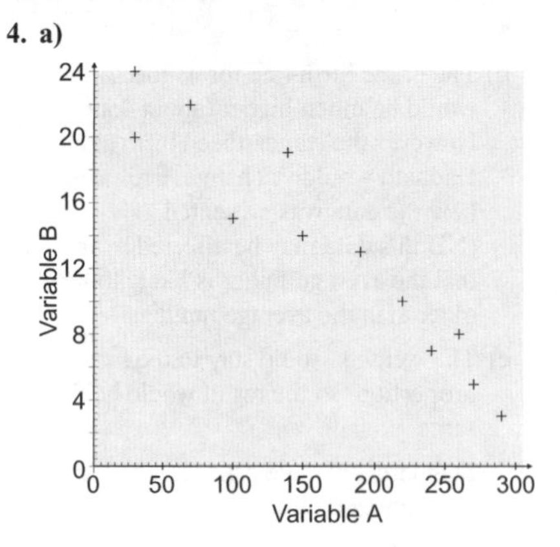

b) The variables are negatively correlated.

Spearman's Rank Correlation Coefficient P.56

1. –1 to 1

2. –0.1 (it is the closest to zero)

3. a) $1 - (6 \times 40)/(10 \times 99) = 0.76$ (to 2 d.p.)

b) Yes. Not unusually similar though (though this does depend how much the women differ).

4. a)

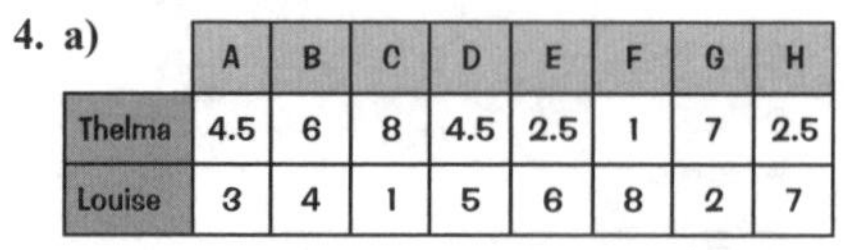

	A	B	C	D	E	F	G	H
Thelma	4.5	6	8	4.5	2.5	1	7	2.5
Louise	3	4	1	5	6	8	2	7

b) $1 - (6 \times 162)/(8 \times 63) = -0.93$ (2 d.p.)

c) They have very different tastes in wine (e.g. preferring red or white wine).

5. a) $1 - (6 \times 2.5)/(7 \times 48) = 0.96$ (2 d.p.)

b) The judges' rankings are in very close agreement.

Working with Scatter Diagrams P.57–58

1. a)

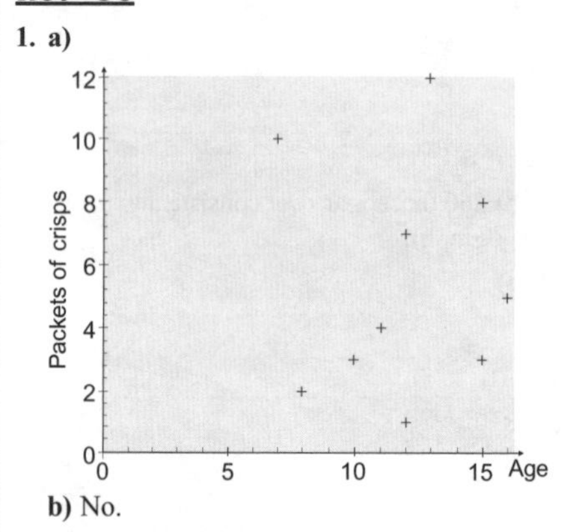

b) No.

2. a) $y = x + 8$

b) The students scored, on average, 8 marks more for paper 2 than paper 1.

3. a)

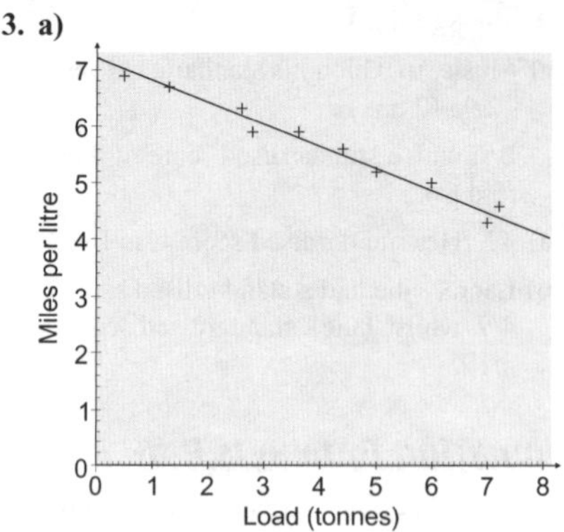

b) Negative correlation. The heavier his load, the more diesel he uses.

c) $m = -2.8/7.2 = -0.39$ (allow –0.38 – –0.40), $c = 7.2$ (allow 7.1 – 7.3)
$y = -0.39x + 7.2$

d) The van does about 7.2 miles per litre of diesel unloaded.

4. a) C

b) F

c) B

d) G

e) A

f) D

g) E

5. a) E

b) A

c) C

d) B

e) F

f) D

g) G

6. a) C

b) B

c) F

d) D

Interpolation and Extrapolation P.59

1. a) Interpolation is estimating a value using surrounding known values.

b) Interpolation usually gives a more reliable estimate than extrapolation, since extrapolation involves estimating a value outside the range of the data set it is based on.

Answers: P.59 – P.64

2. a)

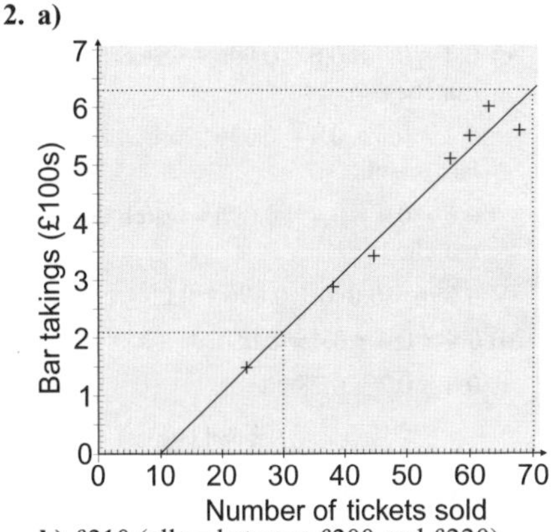

b) £210 (allow between £200 and £220)

c) £630 (allow between £620 and £640)

3. a)

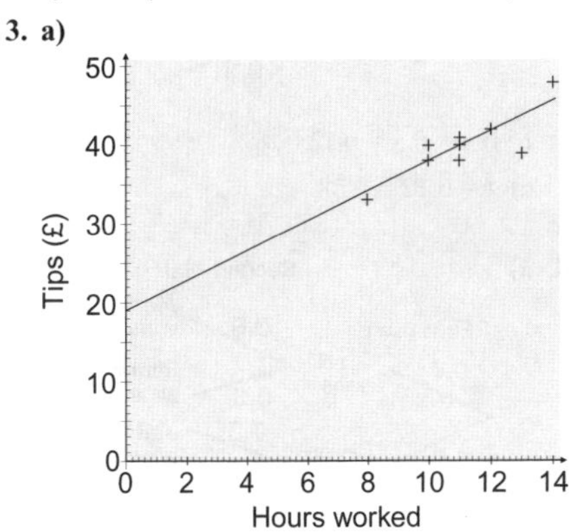

b) $y = 1.9x + 19$.
(accept answer consistent with graph)

c) £91
(accept answer consistent with graph)

d) Her estimate is unlikely to be very accurate, since she is extrapolating a long way outside her data set.

Estimation of Population P.60–61

1. a) 12.25 cm

b) Any sensible answer, e.g.,
If the slug population in Hazel's garden is more than a couple of hundred, 10 slugs isn't a reasonable sample and the answer could be way out.
It's fairly difficult to get an accurate measurement of the length of a slug.
Hazel may have made a mistake in her measurements.

2. a) 40

b) 1200

3. Capture/recapture (or Petersen's method). Also accept any other reasonable answer.

4. a) 20%

b) Most of the students are opposed to top-up fees.

c) More people could have been asked from the same university, but better still would have been if another similar opinion poll had been held at a different university (or several universities) and the results combined.

5. a) 240

b) The population of rabbits can change quite considerably in a week. The ratio used would be less likely to be accurate.

6. 44 800 kg

7. c) 50 (5 would not be a representative sample, 200 is a bigger sample than you need.)

8. a) 120 foxes and 2000 chickens

b) i) 147 foxes and 750 chickens

ii) 500

c) The chicken population is getting smaller whilst the fox population is increasing. The foxes may be eating the chickens.

Section Four — Probability

Probability P.62–63

1.

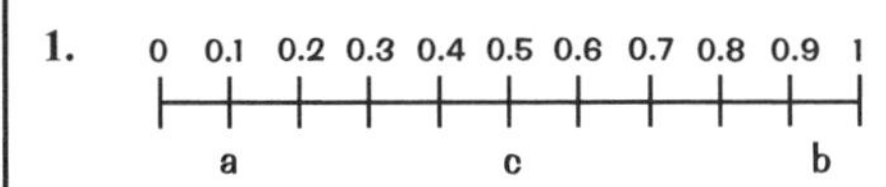

The positions of a, b and c can vary along the scale but should be in the same order.

2. All probabilities lie between 0 and 1, so the probability of Christina passing her exam could at most be 1.
A probability of 1.4 is impossible.

3. The three outcomes are: Glenda wins, Gertrude wins, the race is a draw.

4. a) Spinner 1: **i)** 1 **ii)** 2
Spinner 2: **i)** 2 **ii)** 1
Spinner 3: **i)** 2 **ii)** 1
Spinner 4: **i)** 3 **ii)** 4

b) E.g.

5. a) 1, 2, 3, 4, 5, 6

b) No. For the method to be fair, both must have an equal probability of winning the ticket. Here 4 out of the 6 possible outcomes would result in Gordon winning, so the probability of him winning is:
4/6 = 2/3 or 0.67 (2 d.p.)

c) They should have 3 numbers each, e.g. Gordon wins if a 1, 2 or 3 is thrown and Louise wins for a 4, 5 or 6 (any combination will do). They then each have probability 3/6 = 1/2 of winning the ticket.

6. 1/10 or 0.1

7. P(Picks mint sweet) = 1/4 or 0.25
1/4 = no. of mint sweets/total sweets
1/4 = 7/total, so total = 7 × 4 = 28 sweets in the packet

8. a) i) 1, 3 and 5 are odd numbers, so probability is 3/6 = 1/2 or 0.5

ii) 1/6 or 0.167 (3 d.p.)

iii) 2, 4 and 6 are even numbers, so probability is 3/6 = 1/2 or 0.5

iv) 2, 3, 5 are prime numbers, so probability is 3/6 = 1/2 or 0.5

b) There is one way of throwing a 3 and there are five ways of not throwing a 3. So the odds are 1:5.

9. a) 16 runners are male
so probability is 16/24 = 2/3 or 0.67 (2 d.p.)

b) 16 runners have tracksuits
so probability is 16/24 = 2/3 or 0.67 (2 d.p.)

c) 8 runners are women
so the odds are 8:16 or 1:2

10.a) 50

b) i) 2 red lorries so probability is 2/50 = 1/25 or 0.04

ii) 32 cars so probability is 32/50 = 16/25 or 0.64

iii) 0 green motorbikes so probability is 0/50 = 0

iv) 15 blue vehicles so probability is 15/50 = 3/10 or 0.3

c) 14 lorries so the odds are 14:36 or 7:18.

Sample Space and Venn Diagrams P.64

1.

	1	2	3	4	5
1	1,1	1,2	1,3	1,4	1,5
2	2,1	2,2	2,3	2,4	2,5
3	3,1	3,2	3,3	3,4	3,5
4	4,1	4,2	4,3	4,4	4,5
5	5,1	5,2	5,3	5,4	5,5
6	6,1	6,2	6,3	6,4	6,5

2.

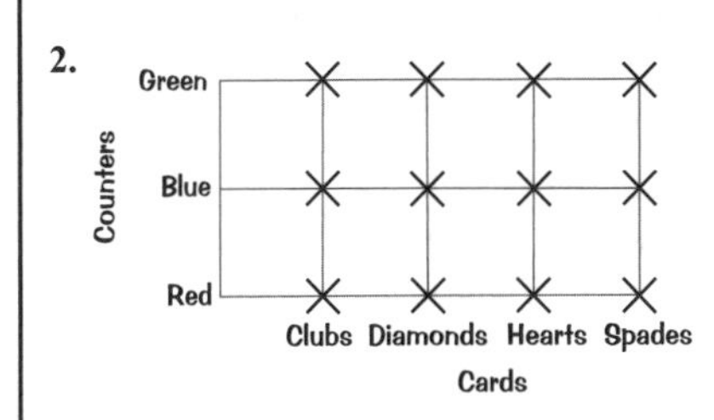

Answers: P.64 – P.69

3. a)

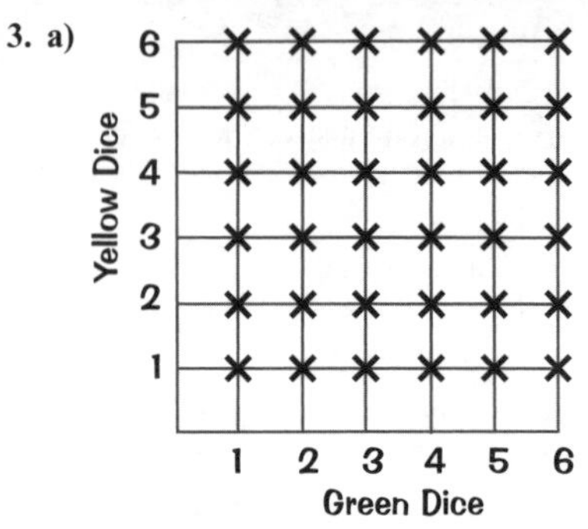

b) i) 9 pairs of odd numbers out of 36 pairs — 9/36 = 1/4 or 0.25

ii) 21 pairs add up to less than 8 — 21/36 = 7/12 or 0.583 (3 d.p.)

iii) 6 pairs have a difference of 3 — 6/36 = 1/6 or 0.167 (3 d.p.)

4. a) 60

b) 15 + 2 + 3 + 4 = 24

c) 3 want to do all three activities — 3/60 = 1/20 or 0.05

d) 14 only want to do orienteering — 14/60 = 7/30 or 0.233 (3 d.p.)

Expected and Relative Frequencies P.65

1. a) 3/6 × 50 = 150/6 = 25

b) factors of 6 are 1, 2, 3, 6
4/6 × 50 = 200/6 = 100/3 or 33.33 (2 d.p.)

c) 1/6 × 50 = 50/6 = 25/3 or 8.33 (2 d.p.)

2. a) 280 × 0.05 = 14

b) 100 × 0.9 = 90

3. a)

Outcome	First	Second	Third or worse
Expected Frequency	10 × 0.7 = 7	10 × 0.2 = 2	10 × 0.1 = 1

b)

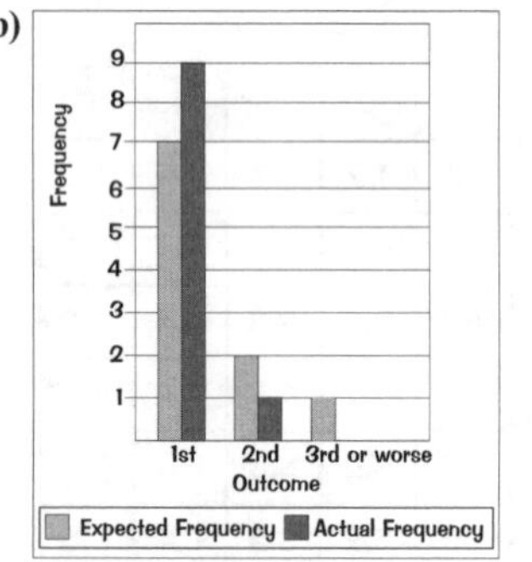

4. a) 45/100 = 9/20 or 0.45

b) For an unbiased standard dice, the probability of throwing a 4 is 1/6 = 0.167. But for this dice the estimated probability is 0.45, which is much higher. This suggests that the dice is biased.

5. a) estimated probability = relative frequency of wins = 5/20 = 1/4 or 0.25

b) expected frequency of wins is 16 × 1/4 = 4. So Dana is more likely to be right.

Probability Laws P.66–67

1. a) not mutually exclusive

b) mutually exclusive

c) not mutually exclusive

d) mutually exclusive

2. a) 3/12 = 1/4 or 0.25

b) 5/12 or 0.417 (3 d.p.)

c) 3/12 + 4/12 = 7/12 or 0.583 (3 d.p.)

3. a) 5/14 or 0.357 (3 d.p.)

b) 6/14 + 5/14 = 11/14 or 0.786 (3 d.p.)

c) 1 – P(action or comedy)
= 1 – 11/14 = 3/14 or 0.214, since the events 'action or comedy' and 'not action or comedy' are exhaustive
or P(science fiction) = 3/14 or 0.214 (3 d.p.)

4. a) 13/52 + 13/52 + 13/52 = 39/52 = 3/4 or 0.75

b) 1 – P(getting a 5) = 1 – 4/52 = 48/52 = 12/13 or 0.923 (3 d.p.)

c) 13/52 + 12/52 – 3/52 = 22/52 = 11/26 or 0.423 (3 d.p.)

d) 4/52 + 13/52 – 1/52 = 16/52 = 4/13 or 0.308 (3 d.p.)

5. probability of Alicia winning = 30/50 = 3/5 or 0.6
probability of Ben winning = 20/50 = 2/5 = 0.4
The events are exhaustive since they are mutually exclusive and their probabilities add up to 1. (Either Alicia wins or Ben wins — there are no other possible outcomes.)

6. a) 1/5 × 1/2 = 1/10 or 0.1

b) 1/5 × 1/2 = 1/10 or 0.1

c) (1/5 × 1/2) + (1/5 × 1/2) = 1/5 or 0.2

7. a) 1/6 × 1/6 × 1/6 × 1/6 × 1/6 × 1/6 × 1/6 = 1/279936 or 0.000 003 57 (3 s.f.)

b) 1:279935

8. a) 0.6 × 0.3 = 0.18

b) (0.6 × 0.7) + (0.4 × 0.3) = 0.54

c) 0.4 × 0.7 = 0.28

9. a) i) 25/60 = 5/12 or 0.417 (to 3 d.p.)

ii) 5/60 × 17/59 = 85/3540 = 17/708 or 0.024 (3 d.p.)

b) 13/60 × 5/59 × 4/58 = 260/205320 = 13/10266 or 0.00127 (3 s.f.)

10. 6/25 × 5/24 × 4/23 = 120/13800 = 1/115 or 0.00870 (3 s.f.)

Tree Diagrams P.68

1. a)

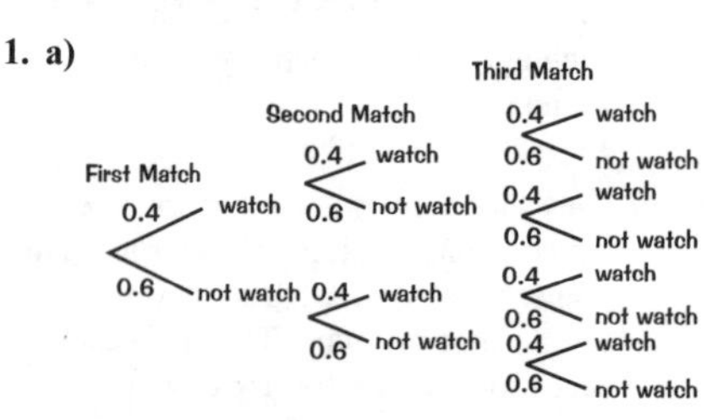

b) 0.4 × 0.4 = 0.16

c) 0.4 × 0.4 × 0.6 = 0.096 – watch first two matches
0.4 × 0.6 × 0.4 = 0.096 – watch first and last match
0.6 × 0.4 × 0.4 = 0.096 – watch last two matches
0.096 + 0.096 + 0.096 = 0.288

d) 0.4 × 0.4 × 0.4 = 0.064

2. 0.4 × 0.7 = 0.28

3. a)

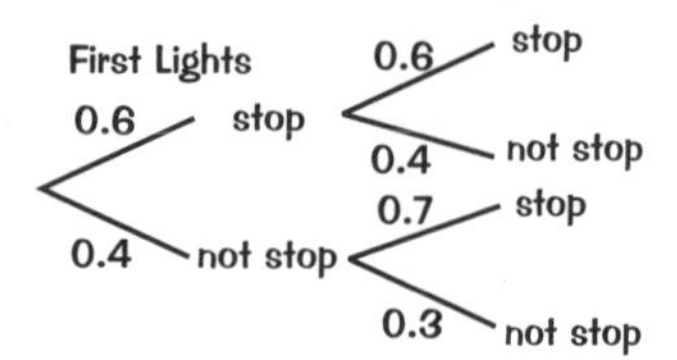

b) 0.4 × 0.3 = 0.12

c) 1 – 0.12 = 0.88

4. a)

Second Match
First Match
0.7 Matt wins
0.3 Simon wins
0.5 Matt wins
0.5 Simon wins
0.8 Matt wins
0.2 Simon wins

b) 0.3 × 0.2 = 0.06

c) (0.7 × 0.5) + (0.3 × 0.8) = 0.59

Discrete Probability Distributions P.69

1. $p^5 + 5p^4q + 10p^3q^2 + 10p^2q^3 + 5pq^4 + q^5$
Expression for the probability that the coin lands on heads 3 times out of 5 is: $10p^3q^2$

2. a) P = 3 × (0.15 × 0.85 × 0.85) = 0.325 (3 d.p.)

b) For n = 7, the term corresponding to two damaged grapes is:
$21 \times 0.15^2 \times 0.85^5 = 0.210$ (3 d.p.)

3. Let the probability of finding a daffodil be d, and the probability of finding a tulip be t.

a) For n = 4:
$1 = d^4 + 4d^3t + 6d^2t^2 + 4dt^3 + t^4$
Probability of 2 tulips = $6d^2t^2 = 0.211$ (3 d.p.)

b) We want 4 daffodils and 2 tulips.
For n = 6, term containing d^4t^2 is $15d^4t^2 = 0.297$ (3 d.p.)

c) We want the terms that correspond to 4, 5, 6 or 7 tulips.
For n = 7:
$1 = d^7 + 7d^6t + 21d^5t^2 + 35d^4t^3 + 35d^3t^4 + 21d^2t^5 + 7dt^6 + t^7$
$P(d \leq 3) = 35d^3t^4 + 21d^2t^5 + 7dt^6 + t^7 = 0.071$ (3 d.p.)